CW00386226

COUNTRY HERITAGE SERIES

Animals

of the British Countryside

W.J. Gordon

ILLUSTRATED BY

R.E. Holding

OMEGA BOOKS

PREFACE.

IN the title of this book the word "animals" is used as embracing the Mammals, Reptiles, and Amphibians, which are, of course, no more specially "animal"—except in the popular sense—than the Birds, Fishes, Molluscs, and Butterflies and Moths dealt with in the four other volumes of the series. The book is on the same plan as these, and its object is the same, namely, the easy identification of our native species by means mainly of external characters and concise descriptions of such habits and peculiarities as help in distinguishing them. In many respects it differs from the very numerous other works on the subject, and is introductory to them all. As compared with "Our Country's Birds" and "Our Country's Fishes," which with it form a complete guide to the British Vertebrates, the number of species is so small that space was found for a few notes on our fossil faunas and separate lists of our Mammals, Reptiles, and Amphibians, past and present.

The illustrations are all by Mr. R. E. Holding, who drew them specially for the work, nearly all of the figures, including the unique series of representative skulls of every British mammalian genus, being from Nature.

W. J. G,

CONTENTS.

ILLUSTRATIONS IN THE TEXT.

CHAPTER I.

LOCAL AND POPULAR NAMES,

———◆———

THIS list contains the popular names, more or less frequent, of the British Mammals, Reptiles, and Amphibians. The numbers refer to the coloured plates, and are those adopted throughout the book.

Adder, 81
Asgal, 87
Aurochs, 49

Badger, 28
Bat, Barbastelle, 4
Bat, Serotine, 5
Bat, Bechstein's, 13
Bat, Common, 9
Bat, Daubenton's, 11
Bat, Great, 7
Bat, Greater Horse-shoe, 1
Bat, Hairy-armed, 8
Bat, Horse-shoe, 1—2
Bat, Leisler's, 8
Bat, Lesser Horse-shoe, 2
Bat, Long-eared, 3
Bat, Mouse-coloured, 14
Bat, Natterer's, 12
Bat, Noctule, 7
Bat, Parti-coloured, 6
Bat, Pipistrelle, 9
Bat, Reddish-Grey, 12
Bat, Rough-legged, 10
Bat Whiskered, 15
Bats, 1—15
Beluga, 64
Blackfish, 67

Blindworm, 75
Brock, 28

Cachalot, 59
Cane, 27
Catamount, 21
Cat-crann, 23
Cat, Wild, 21
Cattle, Cadzow, 49
Cattle, Chartley, 49
Cattle, Chillingham, 49
Cattle, Lyme, 49
Cattle, Wild, 49

Dark Lewkers, 87
Deer, 50—52
Deer, Fallow, 51
Deer, Red, 50
Deer, Roe, 52
Dolphin, Bottlenose, 72
Dolphin, Common, 71
Dolphin, White-beaked, 69
Dolphin, White-sided, 70
Dolphins, 69—72
Dolphins, Short-beaked, 69, 70
Dormouse, 36
Dry Ask, 87

Eft, Warty, 86
Efts, 87
Ermine, 25, 26
Ermine, Irish, 26
Etther, 81
Evet, 87

Ferret, 24
Ferret, Black, 24
Fin Whales, 55—58
Finners, 55—58
Fox, 22
Fox, Cur, 22
Fox, Greyhound, 22
Fox, Hill, 22
Fox, Mastiff, 22
Fox, Terrier, 22
Fox, Welsh, 22
Frog, Common, 82
Frog, Edible, 83
Frog, Green, 83
Frog, Moor, 82
Frog, Scottish, 82

Goldenback, 85
Grampus, 66, 68

Hare, Alpine, 47
Hare, Blue, 47

CHAPTER II.

THE COLOURED PLATES.

————◆————

THE English names in this list are those which are apparently the most frequent in use; they are included in the foregoing list with others, many of which are almost as well known. The genera will be found arranged alphabetically in the fourth, seventh, and eighth chapters, and the species in the tenth. The references are to the pages in which the species are described.

MAMMALIA.

CHIROPTERA.

RHINOLOPHIDÆ.

Plate I.
1. RHINOLOPHUS FERRUM-EQUINUM—Greater Horse-shoe Bat, *p.* 63.
2. RHINOLOPHUS HIPPOSIDERUS—Lesser Horse-shoe Bat, *p.* 63.

VESPERTILIONIDÆ.

3. PLECOTUS AURITUS—Long-eared Bat, *p.* 60.
4. SYNOTUS BARBASTELLUS—Barbastelle, *p.* 67.

Plate II.
5. VESPERUGO SEROTINUS—Serotine, *p.* 72.
6. VESPERUGO DISCOLOR—Parti-coloured Bat, *p.* 72.
7. VESPERUGO NOCTULA—Noctule, *p.* 72.
8. VESPERUGO LEISLERI—Hairy-armed Bat, *p.* 72.
9. VESPERUGO PIPISTRELLUS—Pipistrelle, *p.* 72.

Plate III.
10. VESPERTILIO DASYCNEME—Rough-legged Bat, *p.* 69.
11. VESPERTILIO DAUBENTONI—Daubenton's Bat, *p.* 69.
12. VESPERTILIO NATTERERI—Reddish-grey Bat, *p.* 69.
13. VESPERTILIO BECHSTEINI—Bechstein's Bat, *p.* 69.
14. VESPERTILIO MURINUS—Mouse-coloured Bat, *p.* 70.
15. VESPERTILIO MYSTACINUS—Whiskered Bat, *p.* 70.

REPTILIA.

CHELONIA.

THECOPHORA.

CHELONIDÆ.

ATHECA.

SPHARGIDÆ.

SAURIA.

LACERTILIA.

ANGUIDÆ.

OPHIDIA.

COLUBRIDÆ.

AMPHIBIA.

CHAPTER III.

THE BRITISH MAMMALS:
THEIR ORDERS, FAMILIES, AND GENERA.

———◆———

IN the list of living British mammals we have representatives of only six of the natural orders:—Chiroptera, Insectivora, Carnivora, Rodentia, Ungulata, Cetacea. These are easily distinguishable :—

1. The bats (Chiroptera) have the fore limbs modified for flight.

2. The ungulates (cattle and deer) have the feet hoofed.

3. The cetaceans (whales and dolphins) have no hind limbs externally visible, the fore limbs appear as paddles, and the tail is expanded horizontally into flukes.

4. The rodents have their incisor teeth reduced to two or four in each jaw, which are rootless and chisel-edged; they have no canines, and few or no premolars.

5. The carnivores have four or six incisors in each jaw, well-developed canines, and a shoulder-girdle in which the clavicles are incomplete or non-existent.

6. In the insectivores the clavicles are complete, there are six or eight incisors in the upper jaw, and four or six in the lower, and there are other peculiarities we need not mention, as the order includes, so far as the British Isles are concerned, only the hedgehog and mole, which everyone knows, and the shrews, which are perhaps not unlike rodents, but clearly belong to another group by reason of their front teeth and long snouts.

Accepting these few characters as enough for our present purpose, we can devote our attention to considering the families and genera of which these orders are composed, so far as our country is concerned. And in the usual way we will begin with the bats :—

In these we have to deal with only two families, the first of which is represented by only one genus, which differs from the rest in having leaf-like appendages to its nostrils, and being without an earlet within the ear. To this genus belong our two horse-shoe bats. The other bats have an earlet and no leaf-like appendages to the nostrils. In two of the genera the ears join at their bases, in two they do not join. In the first group we have the long-eared bat

(*Plecotus*), in which the muzzle is hairy, and the barbastelle (*Synotus*), in which the muzzle is bare. In those in which the ears are not united at their junction with the head, one genus (*Vesperugo*) has the ear margin reaching to the angle of the mouth, and there are either one or two upper premolar teeth ; in the other *(Vespertilio)*, the margin of the ear ends alongside the inner edge of the earlet, and there are three upper premolars. These distinctions will, perhaps, be clearer in tabular form, thus :—

CHIROPTERA—

    1. (Rhinolophidæ)—
        Without earlet; nostrils with leaf-like appendages—
        Rhinolophus, 1, 2.

    2. (Vespertilionidæ)—
        With earlet ; nostrils without leaf-like appendages.

        Ears united at base.
          Muzzle hairy—*Plecotus*, 3.
          Muzzle bare—*Synotus*, 4.

        Ears not united at base.
          Ear margin ending near angle of mouth; upper premolars two or one—*Vesperugo*, 5 to 9.

          Ear margin ending opposite inner edge of earlet ; upper premolars three—*Vespertilio*, 10 to 15.

Continuing with the genera, and leaving the species for further consideration, we come to the three families of British insectivores. The first of these is represented by the hedgehog, whose coat of spines is distinctive. Of the other two, one includes only the mole *(Talpa)*, which is without external ears and has the eyes hidden by the fur, the incisor teeth almost level and arranged in a semicircle, and canines in the lower jaw, besides being almost as well known from its external appearance as the hedgehog. In the remaining family the ears are external, the eyes are not hidden in the fur, the tail is long, the first pair of incisors are long, hooked, and point forwards, and there are no canines in the lower jaw. This group contains but two genera, one *(Sorex)* the land shrews, in which the tail is squarish and uniformly haired, the feet are not fringed with hairs, and the teeth number thirty-two ; the other *(Crossopus)*, the water shrew, having the tail fringed on the under surface with long hairs, the feet fringed with hairs, and the teeth numbering thirty. Arranging these as we did the bats, we have :

INSECTIVORA—

    Coat spiny.
    1. (Erinaceidæ)—
        Erinaceus. 16.

Coat not spiny.

2. (Talpidæ)—

> No external ears ; eyes hidden by fur ; incisors nearly
> level and placed in a semicircle ; canines in lower jaw
> —*Talpa*, 17.

3. (Soricidæ)—

> Ears external ; eyes not hidden by fur ; tail long ; first
> pair of incisors long, hooked, and pointing forwards ;
> no canines in lower jaw.
>
> Tail squarish, equally haired, feet not fringed with
> hairs ; thirty-two teeth—*Sorex*, 18, 19.
>
> Tail fringed with long hairs below ; feet fringed with
> hair ; thirty teeth—*Crossopus*, 20.

Of the carnivores we have nine genera, which are distributed
among four of the families, two of the families having each but one
representative, these being the wild cat and the fox. The fourth
family consists of the seals, which differ so obviously from the rest
in the limbs being in the form of flippers, in the hind limbs being
attached to the tail, and in the absence of external ears—so far as
the British batch is concerned—and in the want of the carnassials, or
flesh teeth, which are so marked a feature in the land carnivora. In
one genus of our seals (*Cystophora*), the incisors number two in the
upper jaw and one in the lower, and the head is crested ; in the two
other genera the incisors in the upper jaw number three, and there
are two in the lower ; but these genera are not likely to be mistaken
for one another when the shape of their heads is taken into
consideration, as that of the grey seal (*Halichærus*) is flattened,
while that of the common, ringed and harp seals (*Phoca*) is rounded.
The land carnivores can be sorted out on their hind toes, which
number four in the cat and fox, and five in the Mustelidæ. In the
cat (Felidæ) the muzzle is short ; in the fox (Canidæ) the muzzle is
long, but the four genera of the remaining family are not so easily
disposed of. In two the nose is grooved, in two it is not grooved,
and these latter are not likely to be mistaken for the others as they
are the otter and the badger, the former having webbed feet and
flattened hind claws, the latter being without the webs on the toes
and having the fore claws conspicuously long. But we can sort out
in an easier way the three genera in which the toes are not webbed.
The pine marten (*Mustela*) is sufficiently distinguished from the
others by his long tail ; in the upper jaw he has five teeth behind
the canine and in the lower jaw he has six. Of the two genera with
short tails, *Meles* has a similar arrangement of teeth, while *Putorius*
has only four of these cheek teeth in the upper jaw and five in the
lower, besides having no striking difference in the size of the claws.

This leaves us with—

Carnivora—

1. (Phocidæ)—

> Limbs in the form of flippers ; hind limbs attached to
> tail ; no external ears.

Two upper incisors ; one lower incisor—
Head crested—*Cystophora*, 34.

Three upper incisors ; two lower incisors—
Head flattened—*Halichœrus*, 33.
Head rounded—*Phoca*, 30 to 32.

Four hind toes—

2. (Felidæ)—
Muzzle short—*Felis*, 21.

3. (Canidæ)—
Muzzle long—*Vulpes*, 22.

Five hind toes—
4. (Mustelidæ)—
Toes webbed—*Lutra*, 29.

Toes not webbed—
Tail long—*Mustela*, 23.

Tail short—
Fore claws longer than hind claws—*Meles*, 28.
Fore claws not longer than hind claws—*Putorius*,
24 to 27

In the rodents the feet will also help us. The hares and rabbit (Leporidæ) have four toes on the hind feet and five on the others, and in the only British genus (*Lepus*) the soles of the feet are hairy. In the three other families represented there are five toes on each foot, but the first toe of the fore feet is rudimentary. They can be sorted out by their tails: the squirrel (Sciuridæ) has the tail long and bushy ; the dormouse (Myoxidæ) has it long and hairy ; the mice and rats (Muridæ) have it long and scaly, and the voles belonging to the same family have it short and hairy.

Tabulating as before we have—

RODENTIA—

Hind feet with four toes ; fore-feet with five toes.

1. (Leporidæ)—
Soles of feet hairy—*Lepus*, 46 to 48.

Hind feet with five toes ; fore feet with first toe rudimentary.

2. (Sciuridæ)—
Tail long and bushy ; premolars, two pairs in upper jaw,
one in lower jaw—*Sciurus*, 35.

3. (Myoxidæ)—
Tail long and hairy ; premolars, one pair in each jaw—
Muscardinus, 36.

4. (Muridæ)—
Tail short, or long and scaly ; premolars none—
Tail long and scaly—*Mus*, 37 to 42.
Tail short and hairy—*Microtus*, 43 to 45.

The two families of ungulates are even easier to distinguish. The cattle (Bovidæ) have hollow horns rising from the apex of the skull ; the deer (Cervidæ) have antlers rising from the forehead. The cattle are represented by one genus (Bos), containing only the rather doubtfully wild park cattle of Chillingham and elsewhere. The deer represent but two genera, *Cervus*, including the red deer and fallow deer, and *Capreolus*, comprising only the roe deer, all of which are distinguishable by the form of the antlers.

Thus we have —

Ungulata—

   1. (Bovidæ)—
      Hollow horns rising from apex of skull—*Bos*, 49.

   2. (Cervidæ)—
      Antlers rising from forehead—
         Antlers less than twice as long as head and with only
            three points ; brow tine absent—*Capreolus*, 50.
         Antlers more than twice as long as head, and with more
            than three points ; brow tine present—*Cervus*, 50,
         51.

The cetaceans comprise a score of species, and are not so easily dealt with. To begin with we can take out the whalebone whales (Balænidæ), none of which have teeth. Of these there are three genera, one, *Balæna*, having no dorsal fin, no grooves in the throat, and five digits in the flippers. In the other two the dorsal fin is present, the throat is grooved, and the flippers have five digits ; the flippers in one, *Megaptera*, the hump-back, being long, white, and scalloped, while in the other, *Balænoptera*, comprising our four rorquals, one of which is the biggest whale known, the flippers are short and black or black and white.

The remaining cetaceans have teeth and no whalebone, but with some the teeth in the upper jaw are rudimentary or missing. Of these the sperm whale (*Physeter*) has no dorsal fin worth mentioning, its site being marked by a slight elevation. In the others the dorsal is well developed. The bottle-nose whale (*Hyperoodon*) has it falcate in shape and placed rather far back ; Sowerby's whale (*Mesoplodon*) has it at the hinder third of the body, so has Cuvier's whale (*Ziphius*), distinguished from it by having its single pair of teeth at the extremity of the lower jaw instead of near the middle. With this group we will include Risso's grampus, which is classed with the next family for very sufficient reasons, but happens to be an exception to the rest of his relatives in being toothless in the upper jaw. With his white muzzle and the dorsal halfway between the flippers and the tail, and with from three to seven pairs of teeth at the end of the lower jaw he will come in excellently here.

This leaves us with those having teeth in both jaws, of which some have beaks and some have not. The genera in which the beak is absent, or barely traceable, are five in number, and of each there is but one species. The narwhal (*Monoceros*) is mottled grey above and below, with the left front tooth forming a long spiral tusk, and the right front tooth generally small, but occasionally almost as long. The white whale *(Delphinapterus)* is white both above and below ; the pilot whale, otherwise the blackfish, is black all over except a whitish throat patch, and, occasionally, a narrow stripe along the underparts. The killer *(Orca)* is black above and white from the angle of the mouth downwards, a white patch being conspicuous over the eye, and is famous for the tall dorsal fin and twelve pairs of large conical teeth ; the porpoise *(Phocæna)* is black above and white below, there is no white patch over the eye, and, as is well known, the triangular dorsal fin is of no great elevation, and there are from sixteen to twenty-six pairs of small, spatulate teeth.

This leaves us with the dolphins, in which the beak is more or less prominent. In one genus *(Lagenorhynchus)* it is comparatively short, and the dorsal fin higher than the mouth is long. In the two genera that remain the beak is more noticeable, and the mouth is longer than the dorsal is high. These two are the bottle-nose dolphin *(Tursiops)*, which has from twenty-one to twenty-five pairs of teeth and no grooves in the palate, and the common dolphin *(Delphinus)*, in which there are from forty to sixty pairs of teeth, a grooved palate, and a beak narrow and rather long, without the gradual tapering from the head characteristic of the other. In this way we have obtained—

CETACEA—

Without teeth ; with whalebone.

    1. (Balænidæ)—

        No dorsal fin ; throat not grooved ; five digits in flippers—*Balæna*, 53.

        With dorsal fin ; throat grooved ; four digits in flippers.

            Flippers long, white, and scalloped—*Megaptera*, 54.

            Flippers short, black or black and white—*Balænoptera*, 55 to 58.

With teeth ; without whalebone.

    2. (Physeteridæ)—

        Teeth of upper jaw rudimentary or absent.
            Dorsal fin rudimentary—*Physeter*, 59.
            Dorsal fin well developed.

            Head with crests.
                Teeth in forepart of lower jaw—*Hyperoodon*, 60.
                Teeth, a single pair near middle of lower jaw—*Mesoplodon*, 61.

            Head without crests.
                Teeth, a single pair in front of lower jaw—*Ziphius*, 62.

3. (Delphinidæ)—

Teeth, three to seven pairs in front of lower jaw—
Grampus, 68.

Teeth in both jaws.

Beak absent or inconspicuous.

Mottled grey above and below; long tusk in the
male—*Monoceros*, 63.

White above and below—*Delphinapterus*, 64.

Black above and below, with white throat patch
and occasionally a narrow abdominal stripe—
Globicephalus, 67.

Black above, white below.

White spot over eye; dorsal tall; twelve pairs
of large conical teeth—*Orca*, 66.

No white spot over eye; dorsal low; sixteen to
twenty-six pairs of small spatulate teeth—
Phocæna, 65.

Beak short.

Length of mouth not exceeding height of dorsal
fin—*Lagenorhynchus*, 69, 70.

Beak rather long.

Length of mouth exceeding height of dorsal fin.

Beak tapering; palate not grooved; teeth
twenty-one to twenty-five pairs; lower jaw
longer than upper—*Tursiops*, 72.

Beak elongated; palate grooved; teeth forty to
sixty pairs; jaws equal in length—*Delphinus*,
71.

By the aid of these keys, mere skeleton keys as some of them are,
we can find the genus of any British mammal; but to make
assurance further sure, and for other good reasons, we can with
advantage be a little more technical. It will never do to close this
chapter without a few words on the mammalian orders and families,
though the scope of our work forbids our doing more than touch on
salient differences easily recognisable or useful in identification.

We have been dealing with bats and shrews, cats and foxes,
stoats and seals, mice and rabbits, deer and whales — what
characteristics have they in common that they should be grouped
together? In short, what are mammals? Mammals are crinigerous
vertebrates, even the whales having hairs at some period of life,
though with most of them it is only at an early stage. They are
warm-blooded, and breathe by lungs; and they nourish their young
with milk secreted in cutaneous glands placed in pairs on the
ventral surface. The head is as a rule joined to the body by a neck
—in which there are, with few exceptions, seven vertebræ—and the
backbone is usually prolonged into a tail. The limbs are normally
four in number, terminating in claws, nails, or hoofs, but in some cases

the hinder pair are modified or have disappeared. The skull joins the backbone by means of two occipital condyles. The teeth, when present, are in sockets in the premaxillæ, maxillæ, and mandible. In the higher forms the dentition is heterodont, that is, the teeth are of different kinds, and diphyodont, that is, in two sets, the first, or milk teeth, preceding the permanent series. In one case, at least, there are traces of a pre-milk set, and in a few there seems to be a fourth set. The bones of the skull are firmly united, only the lower jaw and the bones of the ear and tongue being movable. The lower jaw works on the squamosal, the quadrate having become one of the ear ossicles. The upper jaw-bones and palatal-bones form a bony plate dividing off the cheek cavity from the nasal passages: The muscular partition known as the diaphragm separates the thoracic cavity from the abdomen.

The class is divided into two sub-classes, one oviparous, the other viviparous. In the first, Prototheria, the mammæ are represented by a temporary pouch into which the ducts of the milk glands deliver; in the second, Eutheria, which includes the marsupials, in which the pouch is of a different character, there are twelve orders, of which we have six represented in this country, these being, Chiroptera, Insectivora, Carnivora, Rodentia, Ungulata, and Cetacea.

In the Chiroptera the limbs are specially adapted for flight. The presternum is slightly keeled, the scapula triangular, the clavicle long and curved, the humerus strong, the radius long and curved, the ulna rudimentary ; the wrist has six bones, the scaphoid, lunar and cuneiform being consolidated, the thumb is prominent and clawed, and the four long fingers carry the patagium, or thin extension of the skin generally known as the wing, which, as a rule, begins on the shoulder, extends above the humerus and radius to the base of the thumb, forming the antibrachial membrane ; thence it extends between the fingers to the foot, and thence, as the inter-femoral membrane, to the tail ; this lower section being supported by a cartilaginous process, the calcaneum or calcar rising from the inner side of the ankle joint, and bearing on its outer edge the post-calcaneal lobe. The legs are short and weak, the fibula usually rudimentary, and the knee bends inwards, like the elbow, owing to the rotation of the leg outwards by the wing membrane. The bones are slender and have large medullary canals. The backbone is short ; the cervicals are broad owing to the large size of the upper end of the spinal cord, which in the lower portion of the back becomes a mere thread. The ribs are flat ; the pelvis is weak. Some of the bats are frugivorous, some insectivorous, the latter having the longer tails owing to a more powerful steering apparatus being needed for quicker turns in the capture of the prey.

There are two sub-orders, Megachiroptera, of which there are no representatives in this country, and Microchiroptera. In the Micro-chiroptera the crowns of the molars have sharp cusps and transverse grooves, the palate does not extend behind the last molar, the index finger is without a claw. There are five families, of which only two, Rhinolophidæ and Vespertilionidæ, are represented in our list. In both the tail is contained within the interfemoral membrane, or extends very slightly beyond its inner margin; there are two phalanges in the middle finger, the first being extended in repose in a line with the metacarpal, and the middle pair of upper incisors are small and set wide apart from each other.

The Rhinolophidæ have a complex leaf around the nasal apertures, and no tragus, or earlet, in the ears. The premaxillaries are rudimentary and hang from the nasal cartilages, carrying a pair of rudimentary incisors. The first upper premolar is minute, and the lower incisors are tricuspid. The only bone in the index finger is the metacarpal. The skull is large, the nasal bones being expanded to carry the nose leaf; the tail is long and extends to the end of the interfemoral membrane. The only British genus is *Rhinolophus* (Plate I., 1, 2).

The Vespertilionidæ have a tragus and no nose-leaf. The premaxillæ are small, lateral, and wide apart in front. There are two phalanges in the index finger as well as the metacarpal. The skull is not comparatively large, the nasal bones not being expanded. The tail ends at the edge of the interfemoral membrane or very little beyond it. The British genera are *Plecotus, Synotus, Vespertilio,* and *Vesperugo* (Plates I., II., III., 3 to 15).

In the Insectivora the feet are more or less plantigrade, and generally have five digits, all with claws. The skull is low, the cranial cavity small, the facial region long, and the snout projects beyond the lower jaw. There are more than two incisors in the mandible, the canines are generally weak, and the molars are coated with enamel and have tuberculated crowns and well-developed roots. Of the ten families three, Erinaceidæ, Talpidæ, and Soricidæ, are represented in Britain.

The Erinaceidæ have plantigrade feet, with the claws not modified for digging. The radius and ulna are well developed, but the fibula is consolidated with the tibia. The clavicles are long and slender. The skull is without postorbitals, but has a ridge and process in front of the orbit. The nasals are separate; the tympanic is annular, and is not inflated into a bulla. The upper molars are broad with many cusps, the crowns being zigzagged; the first and second upper molars have a central fifth cusp. There is but one genus on the British list, *Erinaceus* (Plate IV., 16).

The Talpidæ have the fore legs more or less modified for digging purposes and placed well forwards. The clavicles and humerus are short. The radius and ulna are well developed. The tibia and fibula are united. The pubic bones are widely separated. The skull is long, with slender zygomatic arches; there are no postorbitals to the frontals; the tympanic forms a bulla. The upper molars are broad with many cusps, the crown being zigzagged; there is no fifth central cusp to the upper molars; the front incisors are not directed forwards. The only British genus is *Talpa* (Plate IV., 17).

The Soricidæ have plantigrade feet with simple claws. The radius and ulna are separate, the tibia and fibula united. The skull is long and narrow; it has no postorbital process to the frontals; the tympanic is annular; there are no zygomatic arches. The upper molars are many-cusped and broad, the crowns being zigzagged;

the upper molars have no central fifth cusp. The nose is pointed; the ears are rounded and flat against the head. There are two genera on our list, *Crossopus* and *Sorex* (Plate IV., 18 to 20).

The Carnivora have four or five toes on each foot, and the toes are generally armed with strong claws. The radius and ulna are distinct, as are the tibia and fibula, the fibula being slender; the scaphoid and lunar are consolidated into one; the clavicles are incomplete or absent. The condyle of the lower jaw is semi-cylindrical, and works in a glenoid cavity of similar form, so that only vertical movement is possible. The incisor teeth are not chisel-shaped; with few exceptions they are three in number on each side of the jaw, the outer pair, especially in the upper jaw, being longer than the rest; the canines are large and slightly recurved; the cheek teeth, except in the seals, are more or less compressed and sharp-edged, and the crowns are not divided into lobes by inflexions of enamel. There are two sub-orders, the Fissipedia, or land carnivores, and the Pinnipedia, or seals. Of the eight families of Fissipedia we have representatives of the Felidæ, the Canidæ, and the Mustelidæ; of the three families of Pinnipedia we have on our list but one, the Phocidæ.

The Felidæ have five toes on the fore feet and four on the hind feet; the foot is rounded and the toe-pads in a regular curve; the claws are sharp, curved, and, except in the hunting leopard, fully retractile. The head is short and more or less rounded. The auditory bulla is dilated and rounded, and is divided by a septum into two chambers. The paroccipital process is flattened against the bulla, and does not project behind. In the upper jaw are three incisors, a canine, three premolars, and only one molar, which is small and transversely extended; in the lower there are three incisors, a canine, only two premolars, and a molar. The outer incisors are the largest. The upper flesh tooth has four lobes, the lower has no inner cusp. There are thirteen dorsal vertebræ. Of this family the only British representative is the Wild Cat (Plate V., 21).

The Canidæ have five toes on the fore feet and four on the hind feet, except in the genus *Lycaon*; the foot is long and the middle toe-pads are in advance of the others; the claws are generally blunt and non-retractile. The head is long, as a rule. The auditory bulla is dilated and rounded, but not divided. The paroccipital process is flattened against the bulla, and projects behind. In the upper jaw there are three incisors, one canine, four premolars, and one, two, three, or four molars, the crowns of which are triangular; in the lower there are three incisors, a canine, four premolars, and two, three, or four molars. The upper flesh tooth has three lobes, the outer one large, conical, and pointing backwards; the lower is very large, and has a bilobed blade, and, generally, an inner cusp. Of this family there is but one British representative, the Fox (Plate V., 22).

The Mustelidæ have five toes on each foot; the claws vary in character. The head is generally long. The auditory bulla is not rounded or divided, and slopes towards the meatus, the lower lip of which is prolonged. The paroccipital process is free from the bulla.

In the upper jaw the molars are reduced to one; in the lower there are frequently two. There are distinct condyloid and glenoid foramina. The genera appearing on our list are *Lutra*, *Meles*, *Mustela*, and *Putorius* (Plates V., VI., VII., 23 to 29).

In the Phocidæ the feet are modified into flippers, on each of which there are five digits ; the hinder pair are joined to the tail by the interdigital membrane. The eyes are large, exposed, and flat. There are no outer ears. The upper incisors are pointed and vary in number; the canines are large; there are four premolars and one molar, and these are flat and pointed, not broad and tuberculated ; there are no flesh teeth. The frontal is without a postorbital process. There are no clavicles. Our list includes three genera of this family, *Cystophora*, *Halichærus*, and *Phoca* (Plates VIII. and IX., 30 to 34).

The Rodentia are distinguished by their long incisors, which have chisel edges owing to the enamel being mainly or entirely on the front surface. These teeth have persistent pulps instead of roots, and consequently grow continuously. The upper incisors are two or four in number, generally two ; the lower are never more than two. There are no canines. The premolars are always less than three, and, in some cases, are wanting. They are separated from the canines by a diastema, the gap being lined by the hairy skin of the face. When present, they are similar to the molars in having tuberculated or laminated crowns. The premaxillaries, containing the basal portions of the upper incisors, are large, and separate the nasals from the maxillaries ; the orbits are not surrounded with bone, and, as a rule, there is no postorbital process. A zygomatic arch is always present. The condyle of the mandible is longitudinal, so that the lower jaw works backwards and forwards. There are twenty-two families, of which four, the Sciuridæ, Myoxidæ, Muridæ, and Leporidæ, are represented in these islands.

In the Sciuridæ there are two upper incisors. The angular portion of the mandible rises sharply from the lower edge of the bony socket of the incisor ; the zygomatic arch is slender ; the frontal is broad ; the postorbital process is long ; the infraorbital opening is small, the palate broad. There are two premolars in the upper jaw and but one in the lower, the outer premolar being small and sometimes deciduous ; the molars are rooted and tubercular. The fibula is distinct ; the tail is cylindrical and bushy ; the eyes and ears are large. The Squirrel is the only British representative (Plate X., 35).

In the Myoxidæ there are two upper incisors. The mandible has a slender coronoid process ; the zygomatic arch is slender ; the frontal is narrow ; there is no postorbital process ; the infraorbital opening is narrow and high. There is only one premolar in the upper jaw, as in the lower ; the molars have roots and transverse folds of enamel. The tibia and fibula are united. The only British representative is the Dormouse (Plate X., 36).

In the Muridæ there are two upper incisors. The zygomatic arch is slender, the jugal is a mere splint ; the frontal is contracted, there is no postorbital process ; the infraorbital opening is high, wide above, and narrow below. There are no premolars. The tibia and fibula are united. The British genera are *Microtus* and *Mus* (Plates XI., XII., XIII., 37 to 45).

In the Leporidæ there are four upper incisors, at birth there are six. The skull is laterally compressed; the postorbital process is large and wing-shaped; the infraorbital opening is small. There are three premolars in the upper jaw, two in the lower ; the molars are without roots and have transverse folds of enamel. The tibia and fibula are united. The hind legs are long ; the tail is short. The only British genus is *Lepus* (Plate XIV.. 46 to 48).

In the Ungulata the toes have hoofs or broad nails, the digits vary in number from one to five, the scaphoid and lunar of the wrist are distinct, the radius and ulna are in some cases united, there are generally no clavicles. The molar teeth have broad crowns, and, as a rule, distinct roots ; they may be " lophodont," that is, traversed by ridges generally transverse to the long axis of the jaw, " buno-dont," with tuberculated crowns, or " selenodont," with crescent-shaped crowns, and " hypsodont," that is, with the crown long and the root short, or " brachyodont," with the crown short and the root long. There are ten sub-orders, of which only one, the Artiodactyla, is represented in these islands.

In the Artiodactyla the digits are even in number, the third and fourth being equal in size or nearly so, and placed one on each side of the median axis of the foot. The femur is without a third tro-chanter. The dorso-lumbar vertebræ are nineteen in number, the ribs are twelve, thirteen, or fourteen. The nasals are not expanded behind. The premolars have one lobe, the molars have two. There are fifteen families, with only two of which, the Bovidæ and Cervidæ, we are here concerned.

In the Bovidæ only the third and fourth digits are functional, and their confluent metapodials form the cannon bones ; the second and fifth digits are incomplete and their metapodials rudimentary or absent. In each jaw are three molars and three premolars in con-tinuous series ; there are no upper incisors and frequently there is no upper canine ; there are three pairs of lower incisors, close to which, and similar in character, is the lower canine. The horns are permanent, and consist of a horny sheath on a bony core. The only British genus is *Bos* (Plate xv., 49).

The Cervidæ differ from the Bovidæ in the horns, when present, being solid, without cores, deciduous, and generally branched. Except in one genus (*Cervulus*) the first and second phalanges of the second and fifth digits are present, frequently with traces of their metapodials. There are two orifices to the tear duct, and the lachrymal bone does not articulate with the nasal owing to the large size of the vacuity. The first molar in both jaws is brachyodont ; the upper canines are generally present and occasionally large. There are two genera on our list, *Capreolus* and *Cervus* (Plates xvi., xvii., and xviii., 50 to 52).

The Cetacea are more or less fish-like in shape. and live in the water, but in no other respect do they resemble fishes. The fore limbs are modified into flippers ; the hind limbs are reduced to rudiments ; the tail is expanded into lateral flukes. The bones are spongy, the cavities filled with oil. There are no clavicles, the scapula, radius and ulna are flattened. There is no sacrum, the first caudal being distinguishable by the chevron bone on its under surface. There are no external ears ; the eye is small ; the nostrils open out near the top of the head, either separately or by a single orifice. The brain is fairly large, its case almost spherical. The facial region of the skull is well developed ; the supra-occipitals rise to meet the frontals by growing over or in between the parietals, the frontals being expanded laterally to roof over the orbit. In front of the narial aperture a beak, consisting of the maxillæ, premaxillæ, vomer, and mesethmoid cartilage, extends forward to form the roof of the mouth. The teeth range from none to many in the adult, but before birth exist in all species. The skin is almost hairless, hairs in the adult appearing only near the mouth. The mammæ are two in number, and situated in depressions on each side of the genital aperture ; from them the milk is injected into the mouth of the young so as to lessen the difficulty of sucking under water. There are three sub-orders—the Mystacoceti, or whalebone whales ; the Odontoceti, or toothed whales ; and the Archæoceti, containing only an extinct genus in which the teeth, unlike those of the Odontoceti, are divisible into incisors, canines and molars. Of the first we have the one family Balænidæ to deal with ; of the second we have the Physeteridæ and the Delphinidæ.

In the Balænidæ, the whalebone takes the place of teeth, these being absorbed before birth. The skull is symmetrical and more or less arched ; the maxillæ does not overlap the orbital process of the frontal ; the branches of the lower jaw arch outwards, and are generally united only by a ligament. The sternum is in one piece, and articulates with one pair of ribs ; the ribs articulate only with the transverse processes of the vertebræ. There are two blowholes. This family is represented in the British list by three genera, *Balæna, Balænoptera,* and *Megaptera* (Plates xix., xx., and xxi., 53 to 58).

In the Physeteridæ there is no whalebone. The teeth in the upper jaw are generally absent or rudimentary, those in the lower jaw are fully developed. The skull is not symmetrical, the maxillæ overlap the orbital process of the frontal ; the branches of the lower jaw are nearly straight, and form a true symphysis. The sternum is in several pieces, and articulates with several pairs of ribs ; the ribs in its vicinity articulate with the bodies of the vertebræ. There is only one blowhole. Of this family there are four genera on our list—*Hyperoodon, Mesoplodon, Physeter,* and *Ziphius* (Plates xxii. and xxiii., 59 to 62).

The Delphinidæ differ mainly from the Physeteridæ in having teeth in both jaws, the teeth as a rule being numerous, and in having the anterior ribs attached to the bodies of the vertebræ by their heads, and to the processes of the vertebræ by a tubercle, while the hinder ribs are attached by the tubercle only. There are nine British genera—*Delphinapterus, Delphinus, Globicephalus, Grampus, Lagenorhynchus, Monodon, Orca, Phocæna,* and *Tursiops* (Plates xxiv., xxv., xxvi., 63 to 72).

There are thus only eighteen families represented among the British mammals, a number so small that, instead of devoting a special chapter to the necessary alphabetical list, we will find room for it here : —

Balænidæ. (CETACEA). Plates xix., xx., xxi.

Balæna, dorsal fin absent, 53.

Megaptera, dorsal fin present, flippers long, white, and scalloped, 54.

Balænoptera, dorsal fin present, flippers short and black or black and white, 55-58.

Bovidæ. (UNGULATA.) Plate xv.

Bos, 49.

Canidæ. (CARNIVORA) Plate v.

Vulpes, 22.

Cervidæ. (UNGULATA.) Plates xvi., xvii., xviii.

Cervus, with brow tine, 50, 51.

Capreolus, without brow tine, 52.

Delphinidæ. (CETACEA.) Plates xxiv., xxv., xxvi.

Upper teeth absent in adults.

Grampus, 68.

Teeth in both jaws in adults.

Delphinus, beak long, jaws equal, sides streaked with colour, 71.

Tursiops, beak long, jaws unequal, sides not streaked with colour, 72.

Lagenorhynchus, beak short and rim-like, 69, 70.

Monoceros, beak absent, mottled grey above and below, 63.

Delphinapterus, beak absent, white above and below, 64.

Globicephalus, beak absent, black above and below, with white throat patch, 67.

Orca, beak absent, black above, white below, with white spot over eye, 66.

Phocæna, beak absent, black above, white below, without white spot over eye, 65.

Erinaceidæ. (INSECTIVORA.) Plate iv,

Erinaceus, 16.

Felidæ. (CARNIVORA.) Plate v.

    Felis, 21.

Leporidæ. (RODENTIA.) Plate xiv.

    Lepus, 46-48.

Muridæ. (RODENTIA). Plates xi., xii., xiii.

    Mus, tail long and scaly, 37-42.
    Microtus, tail short and hairy, 43-45.

Mustelidæ. (CARNIVORA.) Plates v., vi., vii.

    Lutra, toes webbed, 29.
    Mustela, toes not webbed, tail long, 23.
    Putorius, toes not webbed, tail short, 24 27.
    Meles, toes not webbed, tail short, fore claws longer than hind claws, 28.

Myoxidæ. (RODENTIA.) Plate x.

    Muscardinus, 36.

Phocidæ. (CARNIVORA.) Plates viii., ix.

    Cystophora, upper incisors two, lower incisors one, 34.
    Halichærus, upper incisors three, lower incisors two, head flattened, 33.
    Phoca, upper incisors three, lower incisors two, head rounded, 30-32.

Physeteridæ. (CETACEA.) Plates xxii., xxiii.

    Physeter, dorsal fin absent or rudimentary, 59.
    Hyperoodon, dorsal fin well developed, head crested, teeth at outer end of lower jaw, 60.
    Mesoplodon, dorsal fin well developed, head crested, teeth in middle of lower jaw, 61.
    Ziphius, dorsal fin well developed, head without crest, teeth at outer end of lower jaw, 62.

Rhinolophidæ. (CHIROPTERA.) Plate i.

    Rhinolophus 1, 2.

Sciuridæ. (Rodentia.)   Plate x.

   Sciurus, 35.

Soricidæ. (Insectivora.)   Plate iv.

   Sorex, feet not fringed with hairs, 18, 19.

   Crossopus, feet fringed with hairs, 20.

Talpidæ. (Insectivora.)   Plate iv.

   Talpa, 17.

Vespertilionidæ. (Chiroptera.)   Plates i., ii., iii.

   Synotus, ears joining at base, muzzle bare, 4.

   Plecotus, ears joining at base, muzzle hairy, 3.

   Vesperugo, ears not joining at base, ear margin ending near angle
   of mouth, 5-9.

   Vespertilio, ears not joining at base, ear margin ending near inner
   edge of earlet, 10-15.

PLATE 1.

PLATE 2.

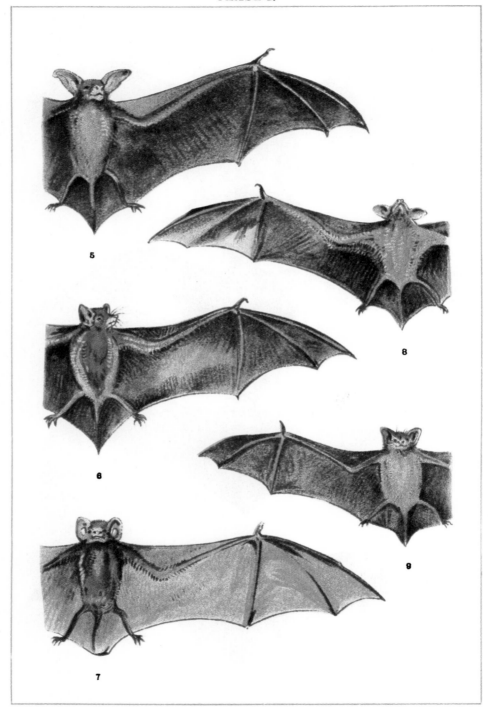

PLATE 3.

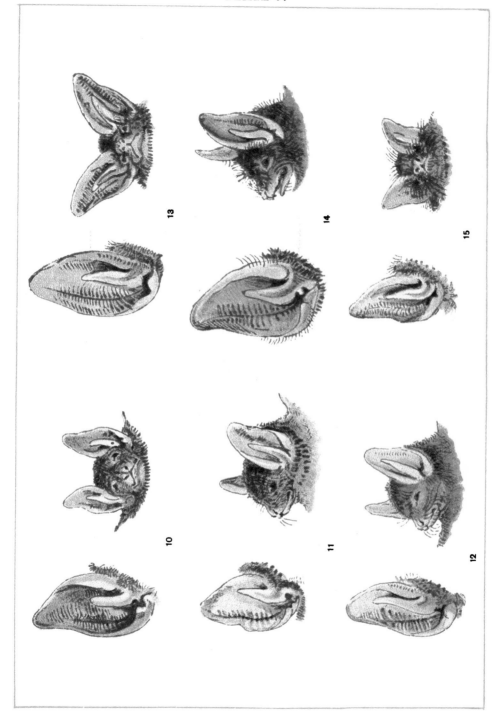

PLATE 4.

PLATE 5.

PLATE 6.

PLATE 7.

PLATE 8.

PLATE 9.

PLATE 10.

PLATE 11.

PLATE 12.

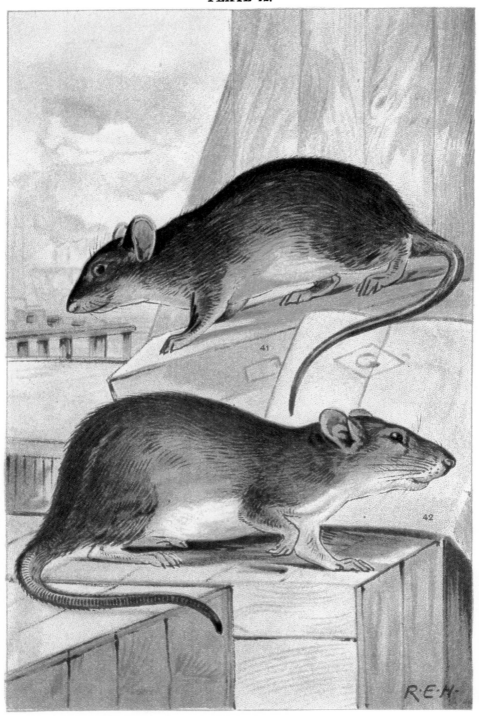

PLATE 13.

PLATE 14.

PLATE 15.

49

R.C.H.

PLATE 17.

51

51 A

R E H

PLATE 18.

PLATE 19.

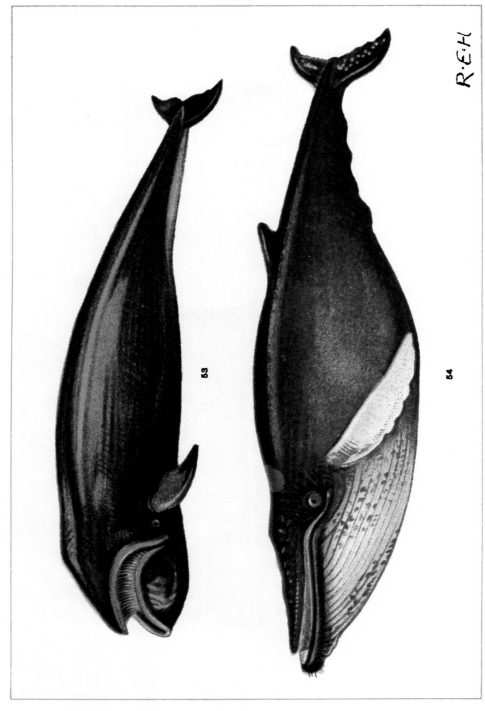

PLATE 20.

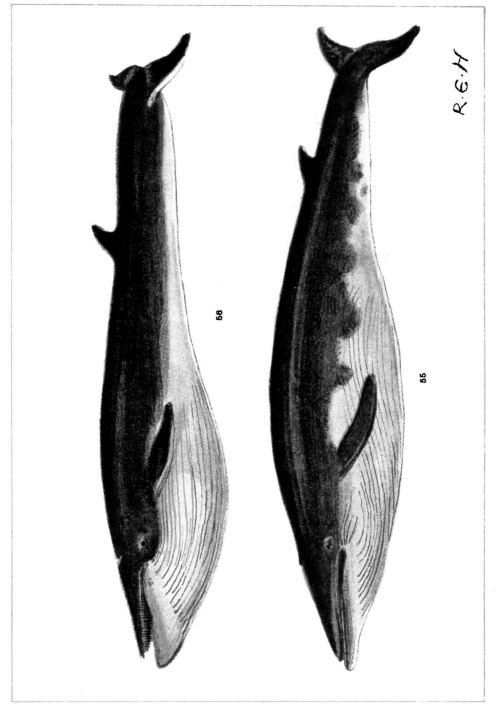

PLATE 21.

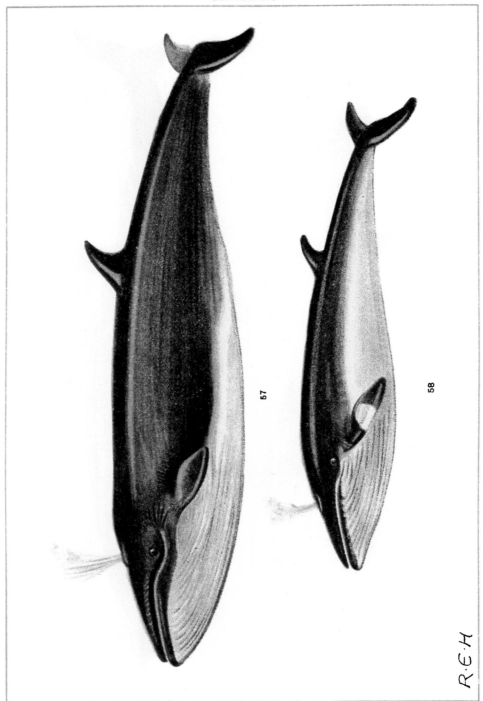

57

58

R·E·H

PLATE 22.

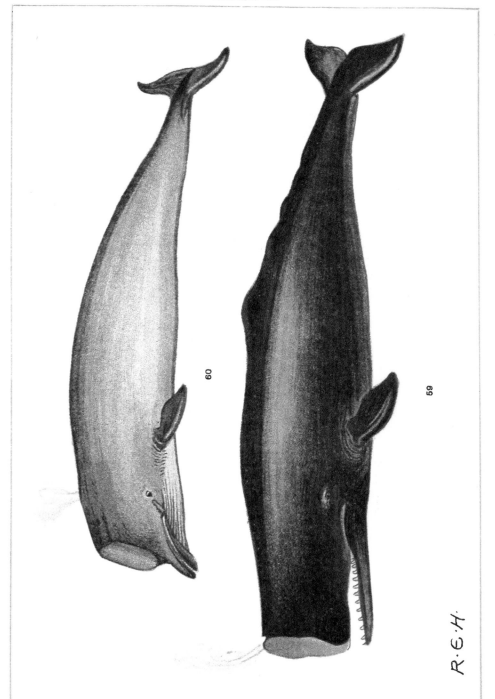

60

59

R.E.H.

PLATE 23.

PLATE 24.

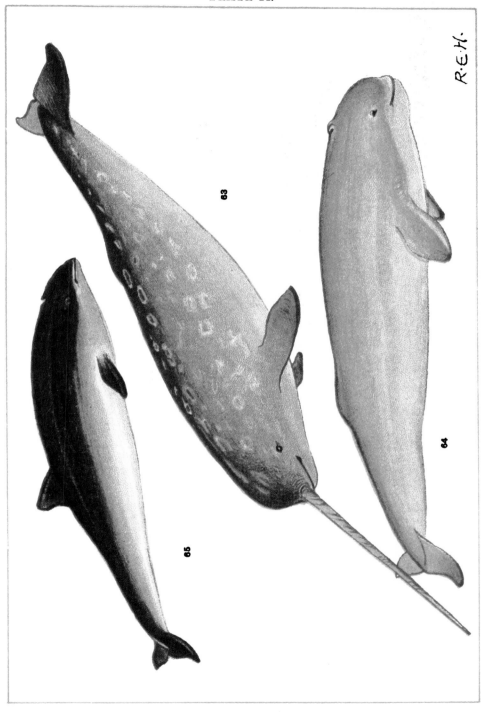

PLATE 25.

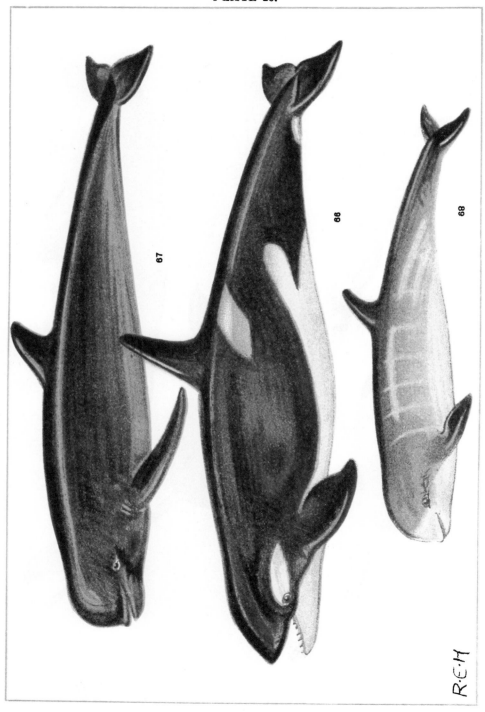

67

66

68

R.E.H

PLATE 26.

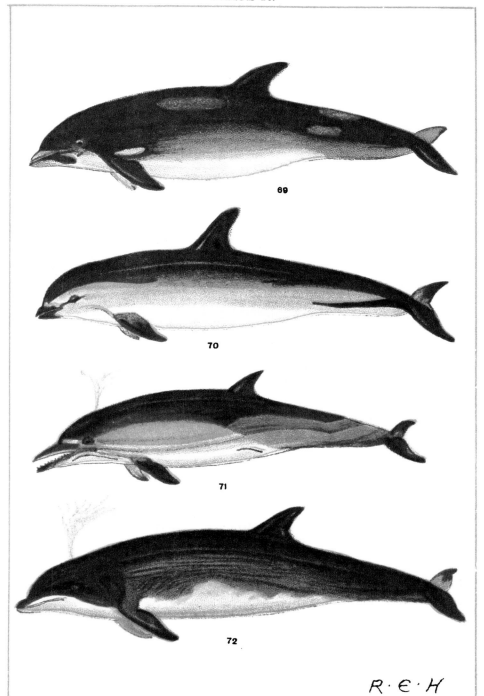

69

70

71

72

R·E·H

PLATE 27.

R·E·H

74

73

PLATE 28.

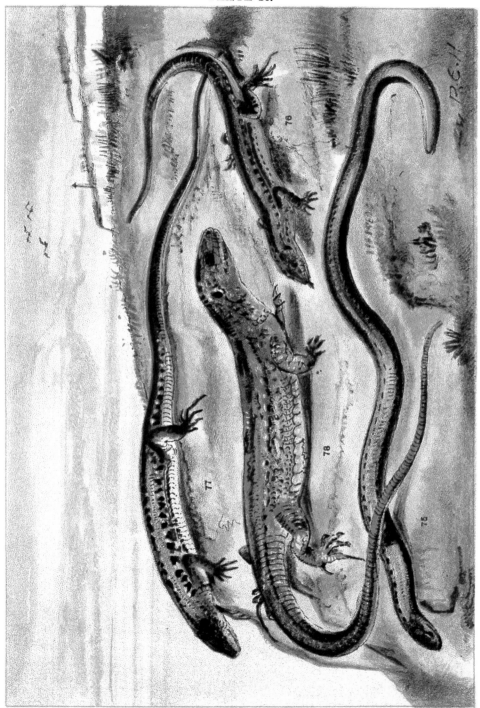

PLATE 29.

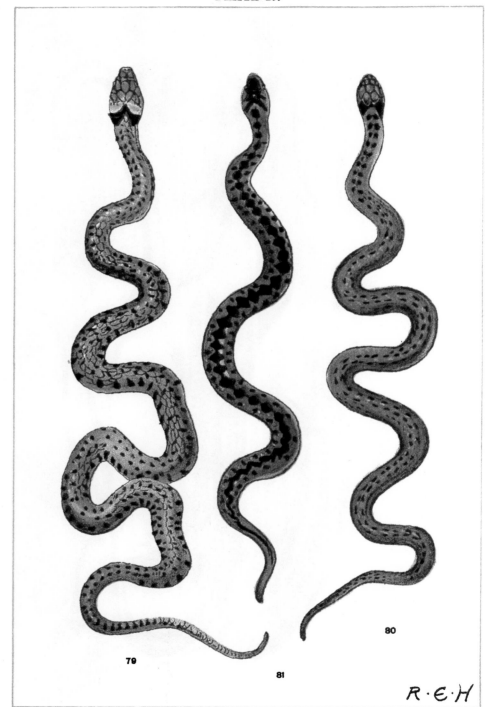

R·E·H

PLATE 30.

82 A

82 B

82

83

R.E.H

PLATE 31.

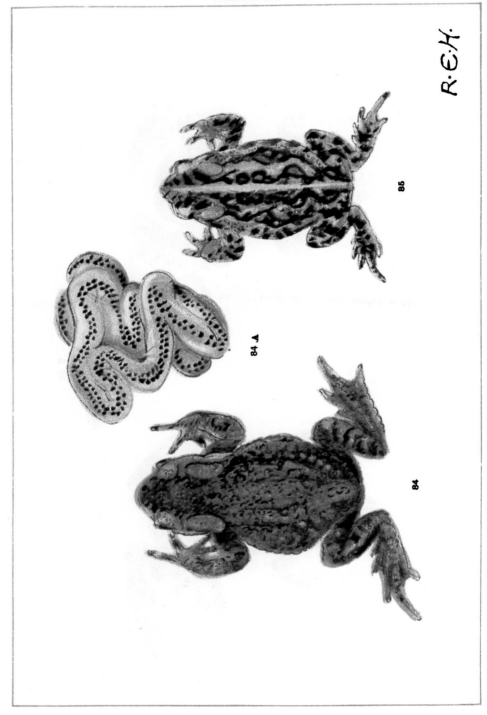

PLATE 32.

86

86 A

86 B

86 C

R·E·H·

PLATE 33.

87

87 A

88

87 B

87 C

CHAPTER IV.

THE BRITISH MAMMALS: THEIR GENERA AND SPECIES.

THE object of this chapter is to give the main distinctions between the species, and other brief notes that may aid in their identification. For the distinctions between the genera the reader must refer to the preceding chapter. The number is that of the coloured figure of the species described.

Balæna.   Plate xix.   *CETACEA.*

53. *australis,*   BISCAY WHALE.   No teeth; no dorsal fin; head a quarter the length of the body; lower lip black and strongly curved.

This large whale, some fifty feet in length, occasionally appears in British waters, and is generally mistaken for the Greenland, or Arctic, whale to which it is very near akin, but which does not range so far south. It is called a "right" whale, as being one of the right sort to catch for its blubber and whalebone; and it differs from the rorquals, or fin-whales, in being without a back fin, in having no grooves on its throat and chest owing to its mouth being so wide that it is unnecessary to dilate it, and in having five digits in the flippers instead of four. There are two blow-holes, each consisting of a straight slit; the eye is very small compared to the size of the head, but is about four times as large as the human eye. There are generally fifteen pairs of ribs, only one pair of which are joined to the heart-shaped breast-bone, and fifty-three vertebræ, being three more than in the Greenland species. It is the "black whale" of the American whalers, and has no white markings about it whatever, and it can be further distinguished from the Greenland species by the curve of the lower lip rising above the level of the eye, by the smaller size of the head, and by the shorter and coarser whalebone. This is black in colour, fraying out at the edge into a fringe of long, tough hairs, and folds back on the sides of the palate when the mouth is closed, the front blades passing below the hinder ones along a channel between the tongue and lower jaw. As the huge mouth opens the whalebone drops down round the aperture like a screen, and by closing the jaws and raising the tongue the whale drives out the water through the hairy fringes, and thereby captures the fishes, molluscs, and crustaceans on which it feeds. It

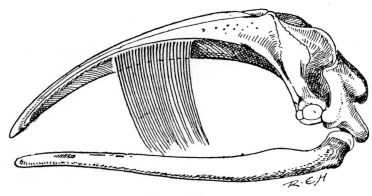

BISCAY WHALE.
(*Balæna australis.*)

was this Biscay, or Southern Right, Whale, that was hunted by the Basques over a thousand years ago. The speed of the right whales does not exceed four knots an hour, except when diving. The baby whale—there is but one at a time—is from ten to fourteen feet long.

Balænoptera. Plates xx. and xxi. *CETACEA.*

55. *sibbaldii,* SIBBALD'S RORQUAL. Flippers black above, white below ; body bluish grey above, under parts yellowish.

56. *musculus,* COMMON RORQUAL. Flippers black above, white below ; body slate grey above, under parts white ; lower jaw grey on left side and white on right side.

57. *borealis,* NORTHERN RORQUAL. Flippers black both above and below.

58. *rostrata,* LESSER RORQUAL. Flippers black above, banded with white.

Sibbald's Rorqual, otherwise the Blue Whale, is the largest animal now living, its length being eighty-five feet, or even more, the specimen that drifted ashore in the Hebrides in the Jubilee year having measured ninety feet. The records of the occasional appearances of this species in British waters begin more than two hundred years ago. Like all the Rorquals, it has rather a small head, the throat expanded when feeding is grooved in repose, a small but well-developed dorsal fin rises from the hinder third of the back, and in the flippers there are four digits, and not five. It spouts higher than any other whale. The body is long and fine in its lines—it can travel at twelve knots an hour—and the flippers average a seventh of its length over all. There are sixty-five vertebræ and sixteen ribs.

The Common Rorqual has sixty-three vertebræ and fifteen ribs, and has been measured up to seventy feet long. The flippers are an eighth of its length, and, like the tail, are dark above and

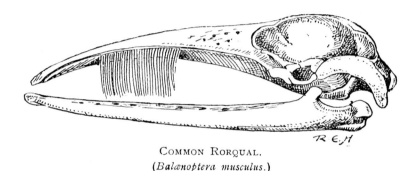

COMMON RORQUAL.
(*Balænoptera musculus.*)

white below. The throat-folds are more numerous than in any other British species. The body is more slenderly built than that of the blue whale, but the possible speed is not so great. This species is a somewhat frequent visitor to British waters, in chase of the herrings and other fishes on which it feeds.

The Northern, or Rudolphi's Rorqual, has from fifty-four to fifty-six vertebræ and thirteen ribs, and rarely exceeds fifty feet in length. The flippers are only an eleventh of the body length, and, like the tail, are black, the colour of the body being bluish black above and white below. In contrast to the short flippers the dorsal fin is higher than in the other species, and placed rather more forward. Representatives of this species have appeared and been captured in the Thames and Medway and elsewhere on the east coast during the last thirty years. One—over thirty-five feet long— was found aground at Tilbury in 1887 with its muzzle nearly level with the river wall, the water in the dock being crowded with sprats, eels, and shrimps, which it seemed to have chased in.

The Lesser Rorqual does not exceed thirty-three feet in length. It has forty-seven vertebræ and eleven ribs, and its flippers are an eighth of its total length. It is longer in the muzzle than the others, and at once distinguishable from them by the white band on its flippers. In colour it is greyish black above and white below, the white extending over the lower surface of its flippers and tail. It is a North Atlantic species, of which there have been frequent captures off and on our east coast. It may be worth noting that Rorqual is merely rorq-val, " the whale with the folds " in the throat.

Bos.   Plate xv. *UNGULATA*.

49.   *taurus*,   PARK CATTLE.   Colour white, with black or red muzzles and ears ; horns white with black tips.

The Park Cattle are the representatives of the wandering herds of Britain restricted to definite areas on the enclosure of the baronial parks many centuries ago, and, owing probably to inter- breeding, are much smaller in stature than their ancestors. There are only four of these herds now left, all of which are white. Three of them have black ears, one, that at Lyme, in Cheshire, has the

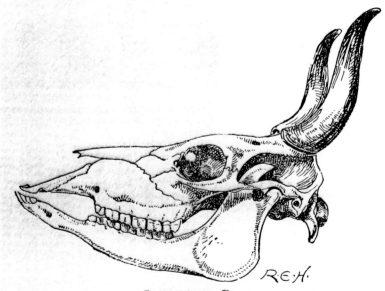

CHILLINGHAM BULL.

(*Bos taurus*.)

ears either black or red, as that at Chillingham, in Northumber- land, had three hundred years ago. The muzzle is of the same colour as the ears. In three herds the horns point upwards, in one, that at Chartley, in Staffordshire, they point outwards. In all cases the neck, sides, and legs are spotted with black ; at Cadzow, in Lanarkshire, the herd has not only black ears and muzzles, but black facings to the forelegs, and the build generally is more that of the highland breed. As with the others, the tail is long, the hoofs large and rounded, and the cows are either horned or hornless. All these cattle feed by night. hide their young, and are difficult of approach and much faster on the move than any of the domestic breeds.

Capreolus. Plate xviii. *UNGULATA.*

52. *caprea,*   ROE DEER. Antlers three-pointed, short, stout, and upright, and without brow tine.

The Roe is the smallest of the British deer, its height at the withers being from twenty-four to twenty-six inches. In colour it is a tawny brown, changing to greyish in winter owing to the tips of the hairs losing their reddish tinge. The doe is always lighter in colour than the buck, and the fawns, of which there are usually two, are yellowish

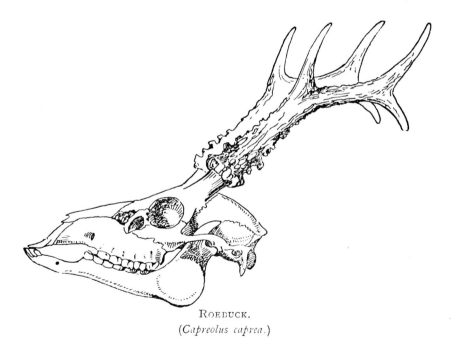

ROEBUCK.
(*Capreolus caprea.*)

red spotted with whitish. The hinder part of the haunches and the under surface of the rudimentary tail are white. The Roebuck sheds his antlers in the autumn—not in the spring—and renews them during the winter. These have no brow-tine, and do not palmate. In the first year they are but a single spike; in the second year they fork, fore and aft, into two; in the third year they have three points, due to the forking of the hinder prong, and they are then complete. They are small but stout, always less than twice the length of the head, and rarely measuring a foot ; and they are round, furrowed, rough, and sharply pointed ; in fact, they furnish most of the so-called " stag's horn " used as handles for carving knives. In the Red Deer and Fallow Deer the lateral metapodials are represented by their upper ends ; in the Roe by the lower ends. There is also a difference in the dentition, the two other British deer having upper canines, while the Roe has the same formula as the cattle and sheep, namely, no incisors and no canines in the upper jaw, three incisors and a canine in the lower, and three premolars and three molars in each. The Roe pairs for life, and is not gregarious ; four at most are seen at a time, consisting of the buck and doe with their two fawns, their favourite haunt being the underwood of large forests, and rising slopes. They are not such good runners as leapers ; their high jumps reach six feet, and their long jumps range from twenty-four to thirty feet. They are the wildest of the native deer, and seldom thrive even in the modified captivity of a large park. They are entirely absent from Ireland, and chiefly met with in Scotland ; in England they are mostly in the north. There are some in the Vale of Blackmoor, in Dorset, and a few in Windsor Forest and Epping Forest ; but these are modern introductions. On the Continent the Roe ranges into Western Asia.

Cervus.   Plates xvi. and xvii.   *UNGULATA.*

50. *elaphus,*   RED DEER.   Antlers without palmations and rounded throughout.

51. *dama,*   FALLOW DEER.   Antlers with palmations and rounded only at base.

The Red and Fallow Deer differ from the Roe Deer in having a brow-tine—projecting close to the burr—and in the antlers having five or more tines, instead of three. The teeth differ in there being a canine in the upper jaw, so that there are thirty-four teeth instead of thirty-two, the full complement being no incisors, one canine, three premolars, and three molars in the upper jaw, and three incisors, one canine, three premolars, and three molars in the other. There is also a difference in the feet, it being the upper ends of the lateral metacarpals and metatarsals that are represented, instead of the lower. They are also of larger build, the height at the withers being Red Deer four feet, Fallow Deer three feet, Roe Deer two feet ; and they shed their antlers in the spring, while the Roe Deer shed theirs in the autumn.

The Red Deer is dark reddish brown in summer, and brownish grey in winter ; the muzzle is blackish, and the inside of the thighs and flanks is of a dark fawn. The tail is shorter than the ear, which is longer than half the head. The antlers are rounded throughout, and are more than twice as long as the head when complete. They first show in the eighth month, and grow as a spike until the third year, when the brow-tine appears. The young deer is then known as a brocket. Next year, as a spire, he has a brow-tine, and a half-developed beam known as an upright ; next year

as a staggard, he has brow-tine, bez-tine or bay-tine (the alter
native spelling giving the pronunciation) and uprights; next yeaı
as a stag he has brow-tine, bez-tine, and trez-tine (tray-tine),
with one upright crocketed, that is, forked into two points, and
the other usually single ; and next year, as a warrantable stag,
or hart, he has brow, bez, and trez tines, with large crockets on

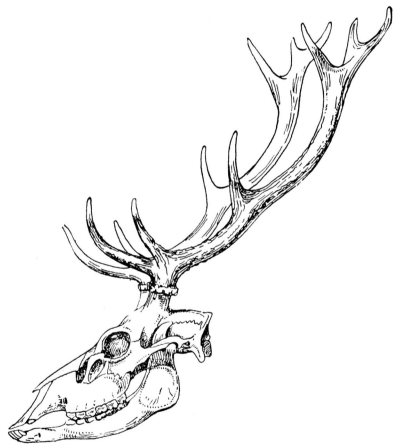

RED DEER.
(*Cervus elaphus.*)

both beams; the next step is when, by further forking, he has
twelve points, six on each antler, and so becomes " royal," the
points of the cup or crown being known as sur-royals. The Red
Deer is polygamous; the female, or hind, is smaller than the hart,
and has no antlers and no throat mane; she begins to breed
when three years old, and has but one fawn, or calf, a year, the

youngster being always spotted with white. The harts live apart from their families except during the breeding season, keeping to the higher ground either alone or in small parties. When they are with the herds the hinds lead the way and act as sentinels, their vigilance in protecting their young making them naturally more on the alert. The herd travels in single file; the flight is always against the wind ; and when matters become desperate it is the master hart that turns to face the danger and give the others a chance of escape. The food consists mainly of herbage and leaves, but includes nuts and fungi and even seaweed. Nowadays Red Deer are practically restricted to the Scottish highlands, but many are kept in private parks. They still run wild on Exmoor and in the Westmoreland hills, and there are a few in the Killarney district in Ireland. At one time they were wild in Epping Forest, but those there now were turned in from Windsor, whither the survivors of the old stock had been removed, so that they may be some of their des cendants.

The Fallow Deer is either fallow—that is faded yellow—brown, marked with white spots and lines, or it is dark brown, the dark brown being, it is said, the old Romano-British race, while the other is of more recent importation for park purposes. Dark or light, there is always a whitish area on the buttocks edged with black, and a blackish line down the back continued to the tip of the tail, the tail being not rudimentary as in the Red Deer, but reaching nearly halfway to the hock. The spotted variety is by far the more numerous, and is larger and has more snags on the antlers. The antlers are large, rounded at the base, and broaden into wide pal-mations. As a rule they have no bez-tine ; the brow-tine is well developed, and, like the trez-tine, is not forked. The antler rises in an unbroken curve from the trez tine, and from the pointed summit sweeps downward and backward, forming a broad curved blade with deep indentations along the edge, the points of which, known as snags, are many, the lowest standing so boldly out from the rest as to be sometimes called the third-tine. Thus this deer has both a trez-tine and a third-tine, the first pointing forwards, the other pointing backwards a little distance above it. The antlers begin to show in the second year as a simple spike ; in the third year the brow and trez tines are developed, and the palmation begins ; in the fourth year the hinder edge is serrated ; in the fifth year the serrations deepen, and the palmation assumes its characteristic form ; and in the sixth year the serrations become so deep as to give the projections the form of snags or short points. The does are smaller than the bucks, and have no antlers; they begin to breed when two years old, and have one fawn at a time, though cases of twins are on record. In the winter the brown variety becomes greyer, but the spotted variety becomes darker, and the white markings become more or less obscure. There are few wild herds of this deer in England beyond those in the New Forest and Epping Forest, but it is the ordinary deer of our parks, and as such is fairly common and familiar. Its true home is in the countries bordering the Mediterranean.

Crossopus.   Plate iv.   *INSECTIVORA.*

20. *fodiens,*   WATER SHREW. Tail and feet fringed with white hairs.

The teeth of the Water Shrew are tipped with reddish brown when young, and become quite white in old age.   There are only thirty of them, those in the upper jaw being three incisors, a canine, two premolars and three molars, the lower jaw having only six, there being no canine, and only one premolar and .two incisors. The front incisors project, the upper ones being somewhat hooked, and the lower pair straight, the skull, as in the land shrews, being long and narrow, though the muzzle is broader and flatter.   The colour varies, but is generally blackish above and whitish below.

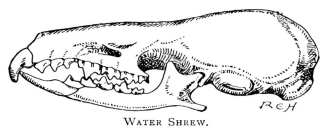

WATER SHREW.
(*Crossopus fodiens.*)

In length the head and body measure rather more than three inches, the tail being about two-thirds as long.   The Water Shrew is quite aquatic in habits, and seems to feed on almost everything small in the animal way, including young fishes and dead birds.   It lives in long, winding burrows in the banks of streams and ponds, and in a bed of herbage in the burrow brings forth and rears its family of half-a-dozen or more young ones.   It is fairly well distributed over England and Scotland, but is not met with in the islands or in Ireland, and it ranges through Europe into Northern Asia.

Cystophora.   Plate ix.   *CARNIVORA.*

34. *cristatus,*   HOODED SEAL.   Webs of hind feet projecting beyond toes ; first and fifth toes longest.

The male of this species is characterised by the large inflatable sac on the nose, which is absent in the female.   The female is a foot shorter than the male, who may measure nine feet or more.   The colour is grey, boldly spotted with grey, the greys being of almost any shade ; the underparts are paler in colour and without spots.   There is an incisor less in each jaw than in the other British seals, the dentition being two incisors, a canine, four premolars, and a molar in the upper jaw, and an incisor, a canine, four premolars, and a molar in the lower.   The teeth are small, all, except the molars, having but one root.   This is an Arctic species rarely found in British waters.   Its young, like those of the Greenland Seal, are born on the ice far away from land, and generally in the month of March. It is confined to the North Atlantic, and is said to be much fiercer in temper

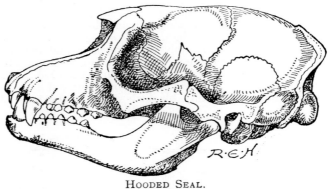

HOODED SEAL.
(*Cystophora cristatus.*)

than its kindred.   Inflating his hood so as to make himself as formidable as possible, the male will fight to the last in defence of his harem, for, unlike our other seals, he is polygamous.

Delphinapterus.   Plate xxiv. *CETACEA.*

64. *leucas,*   WHITE WHALE. Colour white, above and below.

The White Whale, often known as the Beluga, a Russian name given also by the Russians to the Giant Sturgeon, occasionally appears in British waters, now and then, naturally enough, to be

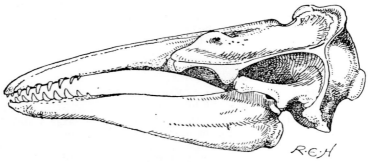

WHITE WHALE.
(*Delphinapterus leucas.*)

caught in a salmon net, quinnat being the favourite food in pursuit of which it travels hundreds of miles up the river Yukon in Alaska. It has a rounded head with more or less of a neck, the head being easy in its movements, owing to the atlas and axis being free.   The skull is long, narrow, and depressed.   There are fifty vertebræ and eleven pairs of ribs, of which eight are double-headed.   There are nine oblique teeth, widely spaced in the fore half of each jaw, irregular in size and arrangement.   The dorsal fin is represented by a low ridge ; the flippers are short, broad, and bluntly pointed ; the tail is not deeply cleft. The length over all ranges up to twenty feet. The young are blackish, becoming in turn mottled, then yellowish, and then white.   The White Whale is generally gregarious, and feeds on cephalopods, crustaceans, and fishes, mostly salmon.   It is the "porpoise" from which comes much of the porpoise-hide—when that hide does not come from the horse.

Delphinus.   Plate xxvi.   *CETACEA.*

71. *delphis,*   COMMON DOLPHIN.   Forehead sloping gradually ; beak long, narrow, and abruptly projecting ; jaws of equal length.

The Dolphin is a southern species wandering into British waters after the shoals of pilchards and herrings.   It is generally caught in the Channel, and rarely off the northern coasts.   In colour it is black above and white below, with black flippers and black tail, and pale brown stripes and grey on the flanks, whatever other tints

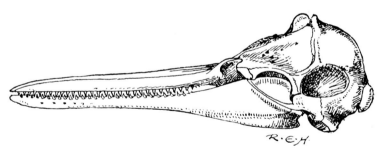

COMMON DOLPHIN.
(*Delphinus delphis.*)

there may be being apparently due to iridescence.   The flippers are narrow and pointed, the second and third digits being large, the others rudimental.   The palatal surface of the maxillaries is deeply grooved ; there are from forty-seven to sixty-five pairs of small teeth all along the beak; and there are from seventy-two to seventy-four vertebræ, and fourteen or fifteen ribs.   The length does not exceed eight feet.   Young dolphins have a moustache of about half a dozen hairs on each side.   Notwithstanding the beak being thicker below, the profile of the head, with the gently curving forehead, large eye, and prominent beak, is not unlike that of the raven.   If this be the dolphin of the heralds and sculptors, we can but pity the poor artists.   Probably that mythical monster was arrived at by confusing this with the fish dolphin, *Coryphæna hippurus*, and combining, from hearsay, the peculiarities of both, without looking at either.

Erinaceus.   Plate iv.   *INSECTIVORA.*

16. *europæus,*   HEDGEHOG.   Coat spiny ; tail short

The Hedgehog is so-called from the pig-like muzzle, which is longer than the short, oval ears.   The neck is short and the tail short, so that the animal can tuck in its legs, head, and tail, and roll itself up into a ball of spines.   In the upper jaw there are three incisor teeth, one canine, three premolars, and three molars ; in the lower are two incisors, a canine, two premolars, and three molars, making ten above and eight below, or

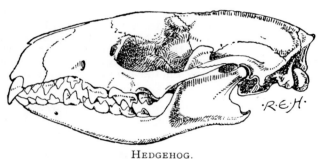

HEDGEHOG.
(*Erinaceus europæus.*)

thirty-six in all ; the largest in the upper jaw being the front incisors, which are nearly twice as long as the others, and have quite a gap between them.   A smaller gap separates the third incisor from the canine, which it somewhat resembles in size and shape.   The second incisor is not so large.   In the lower jaw the incisors are also long and prominent.   In the European hedgehog the canine has but one root ; in the other hedgehogs it has two. There are five toes on each foot, the first being the shortest, and on each sole are five callosities, two on the heel, one under the fifth toe. and two extending beneath the other toes.   The young are generally born in July or August, and are blind and unable to roll themselves up. The spines are then short and colourless, but grow to their full size within a year. when they become whitish with a broad brown band round the middle.   They are striated lengthwise, and are attached by a rounded root, which gives them great freedom of movement. The body is rolled up, and the spines radiated by the *panniculus carnosus* muscle, which starts from the sides of the head, and forms a loop round the region of the tail.   The spines are about an inch in length, and the tail is not much longer than one of them.   The animal is ten inches long or thereabouts, and some five inches high, the legs lifting it but an inch above the ground.   The colour of the upper parts is greyish brown, with a dark streak along the face passing through the eye; on the underparts, where the spines are replaced by hairs and bristles, the colour is lighter.   The eyes are small and black.   The hedgehog feeds on other things than insects, for though peculiarly partial to the domestic black-beetle, otherwise the cockroach, and other insects, it is by no means averse to worms and snails, or to small rodents and reptiles, not excepting snakes, and its depredations as an egg-stealer have frequently been commented on.   It sleeps in almost any hole it can find deep enough or can make so, and the young are born in a roofed nest of leaves and moss.   It is mainly nocturnal in habits, and is generally seen in rainy weather or on moonlight nights, never appearing in the winter, its hibernation being long and complete.   In movement it is by no means sluggish ; the rapidity with which it can assume the ball shape is simply marvellous, and it seems to keep on the move all night long at a man's fastest walking pace.   It is found in all the three kingdoms, and ranges therefrom into Eastern China.

Felis.   Plate v.   *CARNIVORA*.

21.   *catus,*   WILD CAT.   Tail of the same diameter throughout ; claws long, sharp, and retractile.

The Wild Cat can be recognised by its tail, which does not taper like that of the domestic cat, but is cylindrical, and blunt at the end, and ringed and tipped with black.   The fur is as thick as that of a

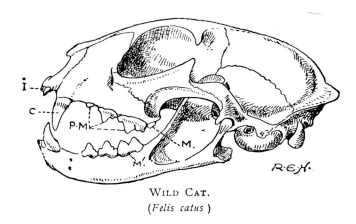

WILD CAT.
(*Felis catus*)

cross between an ordinary cat and a Persian, and in colour is olive grey with tabby markings, the most noticeable being the stripe down the back and two bars on the cheeks.   The toe-pads are not quite black ; the claws are large and the whiskers long.   The head is round, and the tongue is rough, with recurved papillæ. There are thirty teeth, eight in the upper jaw and but seven in the lower, owing to there being two premolars instead of three, the upper series consisting of three incisors (marked i in the illustration), a canine (c), three premolars (p.m), and a molar (m). The third premolar has three lobes and an inner tubercle, and the lower molar (m') has two lobes and no inner cusp. These teeth work against each other like the blades of a pair of scissors, and are known as the carnassials or flesh teeth ; they are sharp and prominent, and the teeth in front of them are pointed and compressed, while those behind, in the upper jaw, are broad and tuberculated, so as not to interfere with their action, the largest teeth in the set being these carnassials and the tusk-like canines. The wild cat lives in wild woodland country in hollow trees, crevices in the rocks, or burrows in the earth, and hunts by night, even the young fawns of the deer being among its victims. In length its head and body measure from twenty-four to thirty inches or more, the tail being about a third as long. The female is smaller and lighter in colour ; the kittens are five or six in number. This cat must not be confused with the domestic cat gone wild, which did not originate from the native species ; it is only known to exist now in the north of Scotland, so far as these islands are concerned, but it ranges through Continental Europe into Northern Asia.

Globicephalus.   Plate xxv. *CETACEA*.

67. *melas,*   PILOT WHALE. Colour black, with the exception of a narrow white area below ; flippers long and narrow.

The Pilot Whale, or Blackfish, is well known on our northern coasts, and used to be widely fished for in the northern islands.

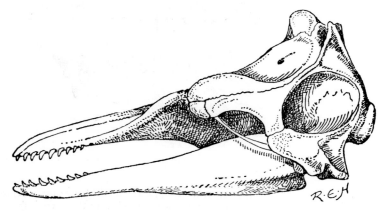

PILOT WHALE.
(*Globicephalus melas.*)

The skull is broad and depressed, but the head is globose, the fore-head rising high and rounding over a cushion of fat. There are ten pairs of teeth, which are small and conical, and confined to the front half of the jaws. The dorsal fin is low and triangular, but the flippers are conspicuously long and falcate. In colour the blackfish would be entirely black were it not for a small patch on the breast, from which an irregular narrow stripe generally leads off along the abdomen. There are fifty-eight or fifty-nine vertebræ and eleven ribs, of which six are double-headed. A noticeable feature of the skull is the great width of the premaxillæ beneath which the maxillæ are hidden.

Grampus.   Plate xxv.   *CETACEA.*

68. *griseus,*   Risso's Grampus. Grey above, with streaks and blotches; muzzle white, flippers grey, tail grey.

Of this species about a dozen examples are on record, but it is nowhere common. The head is rounded, the dorsal broad and high; the tail has narrow flukes, and the flippers are long, narrow, and pointed. The beak widens in front of the maxillary notches, and gently tapers to the obtuse extremity. It is just half as long as the

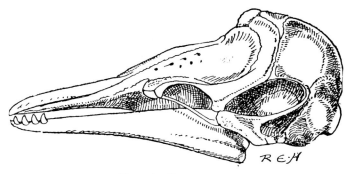

Risso's Grampus.
(*Grampus griseus.*)

skull. The upper jaw is the longer, but there are no teeth in it, the only teeth being from three to seven pairs at the outer end of the lower jaw. The grey colour of the upper parts is often faintly streaked with whitish. The length of this dolphin is fifteen feet or less; it has sixty-eight vertebræ and twelve ribs, of which half are double-headed. It is not happily named, as almost every dolphin, and especially the Killer, is known to seafaring men as a grampus.

Halichœrus.   Plate ix.   *CARNIVORA.*

33.   *grypus,*   GREY SEAL.   Colour grey, spotted and blotched with blackish brown ; whiskers crinkly.

The Grey Seal has a short, somewhat flattened, head, a broad muzzle, and an arched skull.   In the upper jaw are three incisors, a canine, four premolars, and one molar ; in the lower are two incisors, a canine, four premolars, and a molar.   The premolars have but one root, and the crowns are large, conical, and recurved.   It has a claw on each toe, the hind claws being all about the same length.

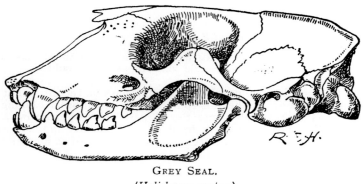

GREY SEAL.
(*Halichœrus grypus.*)

In colour it ranges through almost every shade of grey to the darkest ; in length it has been measured at eight feet.   Like the other seals it would seem to spend much of its time out of water in fine weather.   It is a native species, frequenting rocky islands off the cost of Ireland and among the Shetlands and Hebrides.   It has not as yet been found out of the North Atlantic.   In British waters the young are born in October or thereabouts, but in Norway not until February.

Hyperoodon.   Plate xxii.   *CETACEA.*

60.   *rostratus,*   BOTTLENOSE WHALE.   Skull crested, head elevated ; beak broad and short ; tail without notch.

Twice a year this whale appears off the Shetlands on its migration, and at odd times it is met with off the east coast and even in the English Channel.   It is at once recognisable by its beak, which is more conspicuous in the female, and by its large head, which is of the same character as that of the sperm-whale, but more rounded.   Its only teeth are a pair in the fore part of the lower jaw, which are longer in the males.   The throat is expansible, and therefore grooved.   The eye is in a line with the angle of the mouth.   The blowhole is

like a new moon in shape, with the horns pointing backwards.
There is a well-developed dorsal fin in the hinder third of the back.
The flippers are rounded ; in the male they are a seventh of the
total length, in the female much smaller, only a twelfth. The
length over all is between twenty and thirty feet, and there
are forty-three vertebræ. The first six ribs, being double-headed,
are each attached to two vertebræ. The colour is black above,
grey below, when young, and brownish all over when fully grown.
The females are more numerous than the males and smaller ;

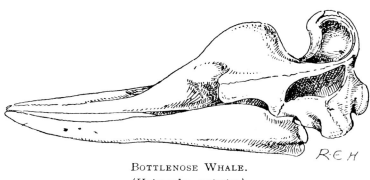

BOTTLENOSE WHALE.
(*Hyperoodon rostratus*.)

the young soon after birth are ten feet long. This whale
feeds almost entirely on cephalopods, and is generally met
with in schools—solitary individuals being, as a rule, old males
—wonderful stories being told of a whole school becoming the prey
of the whaler rather than desert one of their injured comrades. The
Bottlenose always makes a brave fight for life, and can stay under
water for two hours when harpooned. It has been observed to leap
many feet out of the water and turn round its head while in the air
so as to look about, and, as it returns to the waves, to dive in head
first, instead of falling into them sideways like the larger whales.

Lagenorhynchus.   Plate xxvi.   *CETACEA*.

69. *albirostris,*   WHITE-BEAKED DOLPHIN.   Beak and lips white.

70. *acutus,*   WHITE-SIDED DOLPHIN.   Beak and lips black.

Some twenty examples of the White-beaked Dolphin have been
caught in British waters. It is an Arctic species, gregarious in
habit, and seldom straying far south. The head is rather rounded,
the beak little more than a rim, and the dorsal fin and flippers are
narrow and falcate in shape, the flippers being twice as long as the
dorsal is high. The colours are sharply contrasted, purplish black
above, the beak, lips, and under-parts white, with whitish mottled

D

patches on the flanks, behind the blow-hole, and at the root of the tail. In each jaw are twenty-six pairs of teeth ; the vertebræ are

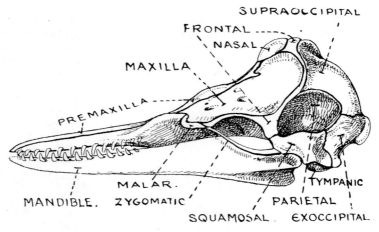

WHITE-BEAKED DOLPHIN.
(*Lagenorhynchus albirostris.*)

ninety-two in number. The largest specimen yet measured was nine feet in length. The figure is lettered to show the remarkable modification of the skull components in this and other genera of the dolphin family.

The White-sided Dolphin is another Arctic species, hunting in companies in pursuit of herrings and other fishes in the Northern

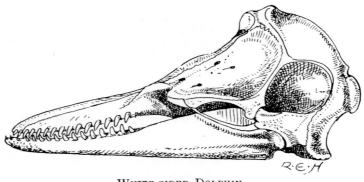

WHITE-SIDED DOLPHIN.
(*Lagenorhynchus acutus.*)

seas, but rarely appearing in British waters. The head is flatter than in the foregoing species ; the dorsal fin is higher, and the narrow flippers not so long.   In colour it is greyish black above, white below, with a brown stripe between, and there are other markings, including a black ring round the eye.   The teeth number from thirty-five to thirty-seven in each jaw ; and there are from seventy-eight to eighty-two vertebræ.   The length over all does not exceed nine feet ; the flippers are thirteen inches long, which is the vertical height of the dorsal fin, and the flukes are twenty-five inches across.

Lepus.   P   xiv.   *RODENTIA*.

46. *europæus,*   COMMON HARE. Ears longer than head ; tail as long as ears and black above. Colour brownish grey in winter.

47. *timidus,*   MOUNTAIN HARE. Ears not longer than head ; tail shorter than ears and leaden grey above. Colour white in winter.

48. *cuniculus,*   RABBIT. Ears not longer than head ; tail longer than ears and blackish above. Colour greyish brown in winter.

In this genus there are two incisors, three premolars, and three molars in the upper jaw, and one incisor, two premolars, and three molars in the lower.   The second pair of incisors in the upper jaw are small and square, the side teeth are rootless, and divided into plates by the enamel folds.   The openings of the skull are all large ; the facial surface of the maxilla is reticulated.   In the gap between the incisors and premolars the hair extends into the mouth on to the inside of the cheek.   The soles of the feet are thickly haired, and the hind legs are longer than the others.   The hind foot has four toes, the fore foot has five.

The Common Hare is brownish grey above, becoming much greyer in the winter when the darker colour shades off more

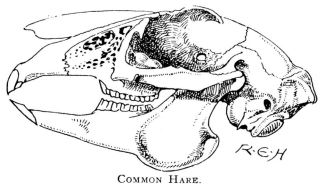

COMMON HARE.
(*Lepus europæus.*)

gradually into the white of the under parts.   The narrow, concave ears are rounded at the tips, which are black for some distance

down.   The short tail is black above and white on the under surface.   The upper lip is thick, bristly, and deeply cleft.   The eyes
have oblong pupils, and are large and prominent, and placed well
round on the head, so as to command almost as complete a circuit
of view as that of a bird.   The body is long and compressed at the
sides, the head and body measuring about twenty-two inches, or six
times the length of the tail.   The hare is strictly a vegetable feeder,
and is mainly nocturnal, spending much of the day in its " form," a
slight hollow in shelter from the sun and wind.   There are three or
four litters a year, none earlier than March or later than August, and
there are three, four, or five young in each ; but, unlike those of the
rabbit, they are not born blind, and are soon left by the mother to
shift for themselves.   This hare is not found in Ireland, but in
Britain it ranges from Cornwall to Caithness, from Kent to Suther-
land, and its area of distribution includes practically the whole of
Europe, except Sweden and Norway, where the only hare is the
next on our list.

   The Mountain Hare varies in colour from light brownish to buff
or leaden grey, and in winter becomes pure white, with the exception of the black ear-tips.   The underparts are white all the year
through.   The tail, in summer, is generally dark grey on the upper
surface.   The head is more rounded than in the common species.
The ears are shorter than the head, and are black for half their
length or so, shading into yellowish grey with a white hinder border.
The head and body measure twenty-one inches at the outside, the tail
being about an eighth of that length.   Its hind legs are also shorter
than those of the Common Hare ; but it is almost as fast on the
move, and leaps quite as far in a similar series of long and short
jumps, the long ones having been measured on the snow up to ten
feet, though as a rule they are about ninety inches, the short ones
averaging forty-five.   This hare is an Arctic species, living during
the winter on lichens and pine seeds, and is found all round the
Northern Hemisphere, being represented in several isolated localities
to the south of its main range.   In Ireland it does not turn white
in the winter ; in Scotland it does.   And as it is the only hare that
turns white, it is obviously the Russian Hare of the provision trade.

   The Rabbit is generally tawny grey above with white under
parts ; the ears have either a small black tip or none at all, and the
conspicuous white tail is always blackish on the upper surface.   The
head and body average some sixteen inches in length, and the tail is
nearly a quarter of that length, and the ears nearly a fifth.   It is
not so flat sided as the hares, and is not so long on the legs, the hind
legs being much shorter in proportion.   Instead of solitarily shel-
tering in a mere form, the Rabbit lives in colonies in burrows of its
own making.   These burrows consist of a central chamber, with
several crooked approaches, and in this retreat, in a nest lined with
the mother's fur, from four to eight blind naked young are born,
which are carefully tended and protected for some time.   The
increase is rapid, as the young begin to breed at eight months, and

there are from four to eight litters a year. From this species have come all the fancy rabbits, and it is of wide distribution, largely owing to the agency of man. It is spread all over the British Isles, including Ireland, and seems to be increasing rather than diminishing in numbers.

Lutra. Plate vii. *CARNIVORA.*

   29. *vulgaris,*   OTTER. Body long ; neck thick ; dark brown in colour ; all toes webbed.

The Otter has a dark chestnut-brown colour of its own, lighter on the throat and breast, the whitish woolly under-fur being concealed beneath a coat of coarse shining hairs in much the same way as in the seals. The head and body average about twenty-eight inches in length, the flattish tapering tail being a trifle over half as long. The

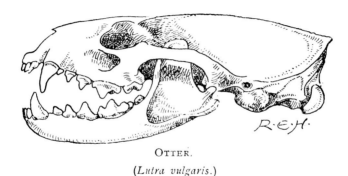

OTTER.

(*Lutra vulgaris.*)

head is broad and flat, the ears hairy, short, and rounded ; the nostrils are a pair of lateral slits closed when diving, the eyes are black and small. The head narrows just behind the orbit—as is clearly shown in the skull—and the neck is almost as thick as the body. The limbs are short and strong, and the toes are webbed and furnished with small curved blunt claws. There are three incisors and a canine in each jaw, and three or four premolars and one molar in the upper jaw, three premolars and two molars in the lower. When there are four upper premolars the first is generally small ; all the premolars have sharp cusps. The blade of the upper flesh tooth, that is, the last premolar, has three cusps and a large sharp inner lobe, but the most characteristic tooth in the jaw is the adjoining upper molar, which is broader than long and almost square in the crown. The male or " dog " otter is larger than the female ; the young are five or less in number, and are generally born in the winter. The otter's home is a hollow in the river bank under the roots of a tree, or a long burrow, the " holt," communicating with the bank at one end, and at the other with the surface of the ground, perhaps ten feet or more away from the river. The prey consists almost entirely of fish.

caught anyhow, to be brought ashore and there eaten head first, the tail being left. The otter hunts in most cases by night all the year round. It ranges throughout northern Europe and Asia, and, though becoming rare, exists in many of the larger British and Irish rivers.

Megaptera.   Plate xix.   *CETACEA.*

   54. *boops,*   Humpback Whale.   Dorsal low ;   flippers long, narrow, and mainly white ; flippers and flukes serrated.

The Humpback Whale has put in several appearances off the east coast of Scotland and elsewhere round our northern coasts. It is about fifty feet in length, and easily recognisable by its white flippers—a third as long as the body—which it frequently lifts above

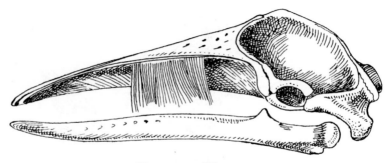

HUMPBACK WHALE.

(*Megaptera boops.*)

the water in flapping itself to get rid of its parasites, or in flapping others as a mark of affection at the beginning of the breeding season. It is the only whalebone whale that has been seen to leap clear above the waves. In colour it is black, frequently marbled with white below. The lower lip is nearly straight, and does not rise above the level of the eye. The throat is grooved ; the whalebone is short, broad, and black. The dorsal fin is low and humplike, hence the name. There are only four digits in the flippers, the third finger being the one that has gone. It feeds upon fishes as well as upon the usual small invertebrates, and is practically world-wide in distribution.

Meles.   Plate vii.   *CARNIVORA.*

   28. *taxus.*   Badger.   Grizzly above, black below.

The Badger is best known by his distinctive colouration, the black limbs and underparts, and the pale grizzly upper parts, with the broad black stripe through the eye and ear. His head and body rarely exceed thirty inches in length, and his tail is about a quarter as long. He stands about twelve inches high, being rather long on the fore feet. His claws are non-retractile, blunt, and slightly curved. His ears are short, his muzzle pointed, his skull ridged, its height half its length, and the lower jaw so deeply locked into the socket as to defy dislocation. In each jaw he has three molars, a canine, and four premolars, and in the upper jaw he has one molar, in the lower two ; his mouth can be distinguished from that of the marten, which has the same dental formulæ, by the upper molar

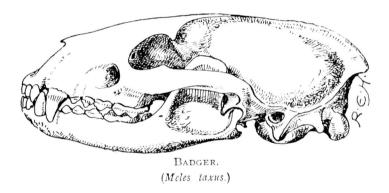

BADGER.

(*Meles taxus.*)

being much larger than the last premolar, and by the lower flesh tooth having a long broad heel. The food consists of almost anything small in the animal way, including insects and wasps' nests, with roots and fruits in addition. It is sought for at night, in the depths of the woods which are the Badger's haunt. The young, three or four in number, are born in a nest of grass laid in the deep burrow known as the " earth," a wonderfully clean, roomy excavation, approached by several subways, in which, during the winter, the owners sleep for three or four months on a bed of dry fern specially gathered for the purpose. There are Badgers in many of our larger woods ; in some they have been introduced after becoming extinct, and the area of distribution includes not only Ireland and Scotland, but much of Europe and Northern Asia.

Mesoplodon. Plate xxiii. *CETACEA.*

61. *bidens,* SOWERBY'S WHALE. Beak long, narrow, and solid ; a pair of flat pointed teeth in the middle of the lower jaw ; skull crested.

This Whale is rare everywhere, and particularly so in British waters. In colour it is black above and white beneath, the flippers and tail being black. In length it measures about eighteen feet or less, and it has forty-six vertebræ. The dorsal fin is in the hinder third of the back. The characteristic beak is rather broad at the base, thereby differing from that in some of the other species of the genus, in one

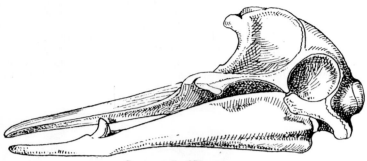

SOWERBY'S WHALE.
(*Mesoplodon bidens*.)

of which the strap-shaped teeth grow to such a size, curving inwards at the point, as to meet over the beak and prevent the mouth from fully opening.

Microtus.   Plate xiii.   *RODENTIA*.

43. *agrestis,*   FIELD VOLE.   Head and body less than 6 inches; greyish above; teeth prisms $\frac{5\ 5\ 6}{9\ 5\ 3}$

44. *amphibius,*   WATER VOLE.   Head and body more than 6 inches; brownish above; teeth prisms $\frac{5\ 4\ 4}{7\ 5\ 3}$

45. *glareolus,*   BANK VOLE.   Head and body less than 6 inches; chestnut above; teeth prisms $\frac{5\ 4\ 5}{7\ 3\ 3}$

The Voles have one pair of incisors and three pairs of molars in each jaw, and no other teeth. The molars are characteristic, each tooth consisting of two short series of triangular prisms alternately placed, the number of prisms differing in each species. In all cases the head is large, the muzzle rounded; the ears and eyes are small, the limbs and tail short, and the build generally is heavier than that of the rats and mice.

The Field Vole is greyish brown above and whitish below, darker on the feet. The soles are bare, and on the hind pair are six pads. The head and body measure about four and a half inches; the tail, which is hairy, is a third of that length. The teeth have no roots. In the upper jaw the third molar has six prisms, the first and second only five: in the lower jaw the third has three prisms, the second five, and the first nine. This is the Vole that causes so much destruction to farms and gardens. It seems to confine its attentions to cultivated land, and is rarely found in woods. It feeds on everything vegetable from root to fruit, and increases rapidly, there being three or four litters in a year of from four to seven at a time, which spend their short infancy in a nest of leaves and moss placed in some sheltered hollow of the ground. It ranges all over Northern and Central Europe, but is not found in Ireland.

The Water Vole is often mis-called the Water Rat, and credited with feeding on birds and fishes, whereas it is a strict vegetarian, and the most harmless of rodents. In general colour it is dark brown, but there is a good deal of black and grey about the thickish fur. Though of aquatic habits, feeding almost entirely on water plants, and living in a long burrow in the bank of the stream or lake, its feet are not webbed. The soles are bare and flesh-coloured, and on the hind pair are five pads. The head and body measure eight inches or over, and the tail is about half as long. The teeth are

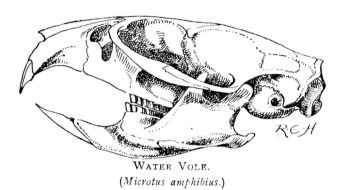

WATER VOLE.
(*Microtus amphibius.*)

rootless. In the upper jaw the third molar has four prisms, so has the second, but the first has five. In the lower jaw the third molar has three prisms, the second five, the first seven. The ears have an operculum, and are so small as to be hidden in the coat. The claws are purple; those on the hind feet are long, those in front are short and compressed. It makes its own burrow, which generally has an entrance below the surface of the water. There are three or four litters in a year, the number of young at a birth ranging from two to seven. It can easily be distinguished from the rats by its bulkier build, inconspicuous ears, and much shorter tail. When undisturbed it swims with its hind legs, and holds its forepaws close to the body. It is found in most British streams, and its area of distribution extends as far east as China, but does not include Ireland.

The Bank, or Red Vole, is chestnut brown, with grey sides and paler underparts, and the dark brown tail is very hairy and whitish on the underside. The head and body measure four inches, which is about double the length of the tail. Unlike the other two species, the molars have well-defined roots, which is so distinctive a feature that this and other voles with similar double-rooted molars have been grouped in a genus by themselves (*Evotomys*). In the upper jaw the third molar has three prisms, the second four, and the first five ; in the lower jaw the third has three prisms, the second three, and the first seven.   Its ears are larger than those of the Field Vole, which it resembles in habits.   Like that species, it has three or four litters in a year of about five at a time, and like it, will occasionally feed on insects ; but it does not limit itself so exclusively to cultivated ground, and frequently settles in the woodlands, burrowing under the roots exposed in the lanes and bye-paths, or taking up its quarters in any deep hole it may find, provided that it be a foot or so above the level of some of the ground outside.   It ranges well up into the north of Scotland, and right across Asia into China.   The usual exception, however, holds good, for there are no Voles in Ireland.

Monodon.   Plate xxiv.   *CETACEA*.

63.   *monoceros*,   NARWHAL.   Colour mottled grey above, white below ; head short, beakless, and rounded ; a long spiral tusk, or two such tusks, in the male.

This is an Arctic species of which as yet only four examples have drifted on to the British coasts.   It derives its name of Nar-whal, the corpse whale, from its corpse-like colour.   In the female all the teeth are rudimental, but in the male the front one on the left-hand side is developed into a long ivory tusk, twisted in a close spiral from left to right.   The corresponding tooth on the right-hand side

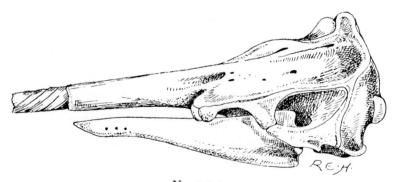

NARWHAL.
(*Monodon monoceros.*)

is generally small, but occasionally similarly developed with a similar sinistral twist.   The dorsal fin is represented by a low ridge ; the flippers are short, broad, and rounded. the second and third digits being nearly equal, and longer than the fourth.   There are fifty vertebræ, of which the atlas and axis are free, and there are twelve ribs, of which eight are double-headed.   The tusk is about half as long as the body, and the body attains a maximum of about fifteen feet.   The Narwhal is gregarious, and feeds on fishes, cuttles, and crustaceans.

Mus. Plates xi. and xii. *RODENTIA.*

Head and body less than five inches—

37. *minutus,* Harvest Mouse. Hind feet brown ; ears short and broad.

38. *sylvaticus,* Wood Mouse. Hind feet long and white ; brownish patch on chest.

39. *sylvaticus wintoni.* Yellow-necked Mouse. Hind feet long and white ; yellow band across chest.

40. *musculus,* Common Mouse. Hind feet greyish ; ears long and rounded.

Head and body more than five inches—

41. *rattus,* Black Rat. Tail longer than head and body.

42. *decumanus,* Brown Rat. Tail shorter than head and body.

The Rats and Mice have no canine teeth and no premolars. The incisors—a single pair—are narrow and have no grooves ; those in the upper jaw are wedge-shaped, those in the lower are compressed and pointed. The molars—three in each jaw—have roots. One of the upper three has about eight tubercles arranged in three rows, the middle row of three being the largest, the next molar has about five also placed in three rows, the third has four only, which are no larger than those in the outer lines of the other teeth. In the fore feet the thumb is rudimentary, and has a nail instead of a claw. The tail is long, round, and ringed with scales The muzzle is more or less pointed and bare at the tip.

The Harvest Mouse is pale orange brown above and white below, the hind feet being brown. In length the head and body measure about two and a half inches, the tail, which is prehensile, or nearly so, being about half an inch less. The ears are broad, and as high as the distance from their base to the throat. The paws are used for grasping, the Harvest Mouse climbing and clinging to a wheat stalk much as a monkey does to a tree ; and a full-size stalk will hardly bend with his weight, for five of these mice go to the ounce. There are half a dozen or so blind, naked young at a time, reared in a globular nest as large as a cricket ball, the aperture of which is closed when the mother is away in search of food. The nest is built among the stalks of standing corn, or, as Gilbert White first found it, suspended in the head of a thistle, " most artificially platted, and composed of the blades of wheat." But the young Harvest Mouse is not always cradled like this, for there are two or more litters in a year. The winter is passed in a burrow in which a small store of food is laid up for use at odd times should the sleep be broken, or it is passed in a rick where corn is plentiful. The food includes worms and insects as well as seeds. Like the dormouse the Harvest Mouse fattens up for the trials of winter, and appears in spring of much more slender build than at other times. He is not found in Ireland, but ranges from the south of Scotland into Siberia.

The Wood Mouse, otherwise the Long-tailed Field Mouse, is about double as large as the foregoing, his head and body measuring nearly four and a half inches and his tail about four.   He is easily recognised by his yellowish brown upper parts, his white underparts with the brown patch on his breast, and his long white feet.   His head is long, and his oblong, oval ears are more than half its length.   The young, from three to five at a time, four or more litters in a year, are reared in a nest in a thick tuft of grass or elsewhere.   The winter is spent in a hole under the trunk of a tree, or similar place, sometimes in an out-building.   This is plentifully stored with acorns, nuts, peas, beans, grain, and sundries, for, during the very partial hibernation, the Wood Mouse wakes often and eats much, and is of so prudent a disposition that he is always prepared for a siege.   He lives and flourishes in several varieties all over Europe, including Ireland.

The Yellow-necked Mouse is reddish grey above, brighter along the flanks and legs.   It has a clear yellowish brown band across the chest in front of the fore legs, about a quarter of an inch wide, spreading out upwards and downwards in the middle.   The eyes are prominent; the ears are large; the tail is long; and the hind feet are long and white.   The skull is an inch and an eighth in length, narrower, longer, and stronger than that of the preceding, and having the superciliary ridges much better developed.   This mouse measures nine inches over all, the tail being about half the length, sometimes rather more, sometimes less.   It was added to the British list in 1894 as *M. flavicollis*, a Scandinavian species from which it differs, and it is now regarded as the most noticeable variety of *M. sylvaticus*.   It is found side by side with the common Wood Mouse in Herefordshire, but does not interbreed with it, just as the small West of Ireland form, *M. sylvaticus celticus*, lives in the Isle of Lewis along with another variety, *M. sylvaticus hebridensis*.

The Common Mouse in its typical form is greyish brown above, and never white below, though it may be of several shades of fulvous or dusky grey.   In head and body it measures three inches and a half, and the tail is as long or longer.   The ears are rounded, and extend to the eye when laid forward.   The eye is black and small.   In both jaws the third molar is diminutive, being about a third the size of the second.   The Common Mouse, though mostly confined to human dwellings, is also met with in the fields.   It is practically omnivorous, with a partiality for most things eaten by man, and is reared in a comfortable nest made of small pieces of straw, frag-ments of dress material, paper, and other household sundries.   The female begins to breed when less than a year old, and she has five or more litters a year, and from four to seven in a litter, the young being born blind and naked, but developing so quickly as to be able to shift for themselves in a fortnight.   Now and then they sport, and from these variations have come the fancy mice of several colours, including the usual albino, of which boys and others have made pets, which is seldom the fate of the typical form, though it seems to be the in-evitable companion of man.

The Black Rat is blackish above and ashy below, with flesh-:oloured legs and feet.   The head is slender, the muzzle sharp and

projecting beyond the lips, the ears are ovate and not covered with
much hair; the eyes are large and the whiskers long.   The head
and body measure about seven inches, and the tail is always as long, if
not longer, being generally longer in the male than in tne female.
It eats almost anything, though not so carnivorous as the Brown
Rat, and as MacGillivray suggested, would be an interesting animal
if it kept out of human dwellings, and did less damage in pursuit
of its food.   Its young are born blind, seven, eight, or nine of them
at a time, and there are two or three litters a year; but it is now
becoming rare in this country, owing to its enemies being so many,
chief among them being the Brown Rat, which is just as cosmo-
politan and is superseding it almost everywhere.

The Brown Rat may be nine inches long in the head and body,
which are always an inch or so longer than the tail.   In colour it is
greyish brown above, darkest on the back, and whitish below, the
ears, feet, and tail being flesh-coloured.   In build it is rather stout,
with a large head, blunt muzzle, rounded ears, and a conspicuously
long foot.   As in the Black Rat, the proximal pad on the sole of the
foot is double the length of the next pad, a distinguishing mark

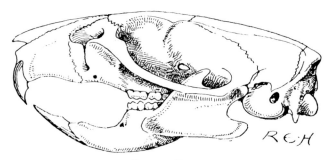

BROWN RAT.
(*Mus decumanus.*)

between these rats and the Common Mouse, in which this pad is
generally rounded, and never double as long as the one adjoining.
The Brown Rat is the common rat, the rat of the drains and sewers,
a truly miscellaneous eater, who will gnaw anything, even elephants'
tusks and water pipes, and does damage to almost everything useful
to man.   He would have been wiped off the British list long since
were it not for his fecundity, the female beginning to breed at six
months, there being nine or ten young at a time, and four or more
litters in a year.   He seems somehow to have got into Kirkdale
cave during an early voyage of discovery of uncertain date, but
the general impression is that he introduced himself to these
islands a century or so ago, as the Black Rat had done before
him, and he has distributed himself all over the world.

Muscardinus.   Plate x.   *RODENTIA*.

36.   *avellanarius*, Dormouse.   Colour of upper parts tawny russet ; tail
hairy and of the same diameter throughout.

The Dormouse is of a pale tawny brown above and yellowish
below, with a white patch on the throat extending between the legs.
The head is rather large, the ears are about a third of its length ;
the eyes are black, bright, and prominent ; the nose is pointed.
The arms are shorter than the legs, and the thumb is rudimentary ;
all the paws are padded and are used like hands, but the claws are
neither so long nor so strong as those of the squirrel.   There are an
incisor, a premolar, and three molars in each jaw, the side teeth
having the crowns flat and the enamel transversely folded.   The Dormouse is about six inches over all, of which the tail is rather less than
half.   He sleeps for five or six months, and fattens himself for the
experience, so that by the end of September he is very plump in the
body ; the fat is used up during the hibernation, and when he wakes
for good in the spring he is particularly gaunt and hungry-looking.

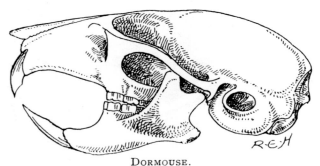

Dormouse.
(*Muscardinus avellanarius.*)

In habit he is nocturnal, and seeks his food among thickets and hedge-
rows, on the bushes and smaller trees.   He feeds on nuts and fruits,
and in manner is a small squirrel, but instead of picking the nuts to
begin with, will often bore a hole into them and extract the kernel
in fragments as they hang on the bough.   He will also eat grain and
other seeds, and caterpillars and other insects do not come amiss
to him when they are within easy reach.   For winter quarters he
builds a globular nest which he stores with provisions, and on these
he feeds when he occasionally awakens, but the quantity is small,
and barely enough to tide him through the period when other food is
unprocurable   The young, three or four in number, are born blind and
naked, and wear a grey coat in their infancy which reddens as they
grow up.   Their home is a neatly-made globular nest built a yard or
so above the ground.   The Dormouse is not found in Ireland or in
he North of Scotland, nor does it range out of Europe.

Mustela.   Plate v.   *CARNIVORA.*

23. *martes,*   Pine Marten.   Colour livery brown, throat dark buff, chest whitish.

There is a pleasant intelligent look about the Marten which has gained him many friends at first sight. With a good head, good eyes, well-proportioned ears and clean-cut muzzle, he is certainly the nicest-looking of his family. His broad, rounded ears are furred on both sides, his tail is bushy, and his colour a distinctive brown un-like that of any other British animal, the stone-grey under-fur not showing through the upper coat as in the polecat. The skull is rather long. There are thirty-eight teeth, three incisors, one canine, and four premolars in each jaw, and one molar in the upper set and two in the lower, so that there is a molar more in both jaws than in the dogs and one lower molar more than in the cats. The lower incisors are smaller than the upper, the canines are long and sharp, and the carnassials,

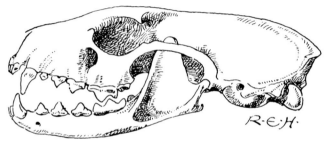

Pine Marten.
(*Mustela martes.*)

sectorials, or flesh-teeth, whichever one may choose to call them, are, as usual, the fourth upper premolar and the lower first molar, the latter of which has a bilobed blade, a small inner cusp, and a heel about a third as long as the length of the tooth. The nose projects a little beyond the lips; the tongue is smooth; the body is long and supple; the limbs are short, the feet rounded, their soles furred; and there are five toes on each foot, the claws being semi-retractile. The Marten lives in the woods and hunts in the trees, leaping from bough to bough like a squirrel; in rocky country it may be found in the open in pursuit of rabbits, and then it shelters in some hole in a crag, but as a rule its home is in a hollow trunk, or in a magpie's nest, or squirrel's drey. There are about half a dozen young at a time and two litters in a year. The female resembles the male; the tail is a foot or thereabouts in length, the head and body being half as long again. The Marten is said, some-what doubtfully, to exist in Epping Forest and other woodlands in the south, and is certainly met with here and there throughout Britain and Ireland, oftenest in the Lake district, but is yearly becoming rarer.   He ranges into Northern Asia, where he is replaced by his next-of-kin, the sable.

Orca.   Plate xxv.   *CETACEA.*

66.   *gladiator,*   KILLER.   Black above, with a white patch over the eye ; lower jaw white ; back fin large and powerful.

The Killer, recognisable from afar by its tall back-fin and close at hand by its white eye-patch, feeds mainly on other dolphins, whales, and seals, and appears wherever they are, and sometimes where they are not, as, for instance, in the Thames off Battersea Park.   The head is depressed, the snout rounded, the body stout, the flippers large, ovate, and nearly as broad as long.   The dorsal rises in the middle of the back, and sometimes there is a white patch behind it in addition to that above the eye.   The white from below

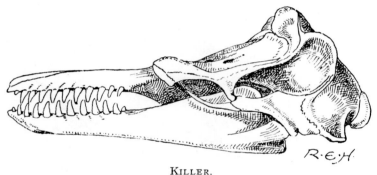

KILLER.
(*Orca gladiator.*)

extends up the side behind the dorsal, to form a promontory pointing backwards.   The teeth are large, with conical crowns, and number from ten to thirteen pairs, placed all along each jaw.   There are fifty-two vertebræ and twelve ribs, seven of which are double-headed.   The Killer is twenty feet or more in length, and is excelled in voracity by nothing alive.

Phoca.   Plate viii.   *CARNIVORA.*

30.   *vitulina,*   COMMON SEAL.   Teeth contiguous and set obliquely ; colour yellowish grey with dark spots.

31.   *hispida,*   RINGED SEAL.   Teeth separate and set straight ; colour blackish grey with oval rings.

32.   *grœnlandica,*   HARP SEAL.   Teeth separate and set straight ; colour grey with curved black bars.

These seals have no ears, and the coat is hairy, with no woolly under-fur.   The head is round and short, and the fore feet are short, with strong claws.   There are three incisors, a canine, four premolars, and a molar in the upper jaw, and an incisor less in the lower jaw ; the molars and premolars are small and pointed, with three or four cusps, and most of them have two roots. The eye is large and fully open in water, but half closed in air. Respiration is slow, as in all seals, there being a two minutes' interval between each breath. A seal can remain submerged for a quarter of an hour or thereabouts, but the baby seal has always to be coaxed or forced by its parents to enter the water. The Common Seal breeds on shore, generally on an island, the others breed on the ice, but in all the young are born white, as if to be invisible amid snow, but they become greyish before taking to the sea. All three species are gregarious, especially the Harp Seal; only one is native, but no seal is claimed as British on the strength of its having drifted ashore, the reason being that a seal sinks as it dies.

The Common Seal rarely exceeds five feet in length ; in colour it may be averaged as yellowish grey with black and brown spots, the under parts being paler and unspotted. The colour varies greatly, but as a rule the male is darker than the female. This species can always be distinguished by the compact, oblique setting of the side teeth. The skull is thicker and proportionately larger than in the other species ; the branches of the lower jaw are parallel to start

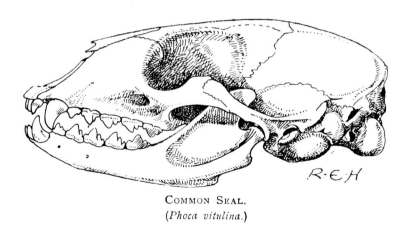

COMMON SEAL.
(*Phoca vitulina.*)

with, the premaxillaries are not laterally contiguous with the nasals, and the after edge of the palate is deeply notched. The Common Seal feeds mainly on fishes, and remains in the same localities all the year through. It breeds on the smaller islands off the British coasts ; it is met with in the North Pacific as well as the North Atlantic, but though ranging well north does not frequent the ice. The young are born in May or June, there being one, occasionally two, at a birth.

The Ringed Seal is smaller and not so stoutly built, its length being generally under four feet. It is blackish grey in colour, the

E

markings taking the form of whitish oval rings on the back and flanks. The head is rather narrow. The teeth have intervals between them, and are not obliquely set in the jaw; the branches of the lower jaw, as in the Harp Seal, are parallel to begin with ; the premaxillaries are laterally contiguous with the nasals ; and the hinder edge of the palate is deeply notched, as in the Common Seal. The thumb is noticeably longer than the other digits. This species is a summer visitor from the far north, where it frequents the coast and breeds on the ice, the young—never more than one a year—being born in the early spring. It is found in the North Pacific as well as in the North Atlantic.

The Harp Seal is from five to six feet long. In colour it is a pale tawny or yellowish grey with a dark half-moon on the shoulder and flank, the two curves forming the so-called " harp " or " saddle." In the females the mark is generally present but much less distinct ; the males being otherwise distinguishable by their black faces. The head is rather dog-like. The teeth are not set obliquely, and are well spaced ; the branches of the lower jaw, owing to the long symphysis, nearly meet for a third of the length ; the premaxillaries are not laterally contiguous with the nasals ; and the hinder edge of the palate is not notched or only faintly so. This is the Greenland Seal, another summer visitor from high latitudes. Unlike the Ringed Seal it does not frequent the ice-bound coasts of the north and betake itself to the floes when the ice breaks up for its young to be born on them, but chooses the fields and floes in the open sea as if they were so many islands. It is, however, only certain regions of the Arctic that it visits as its breeding grounds, and thither it migrates in thousands every year. It differs from the Ringed Seal, also, in never making a breathing-hole, for unlike that species it does not get under the ice, but seeks its prey—consisting of fishes, molluscs, and crustaceans—round the edges. The young, generally one, sometimes two, seldom three, are born in March, and are a fortnight or three weeks before they take to the water. This is the seal of the Atlantic trade—the earless one that yields the oil and the hairy skins that are made into leather. It is also found in the Pacific, but there it is left in peace, the seal of the Pacific trade being the eared species that yields the furry skins that are made into jackets.

Phocæ.   Plate xxiv. *CETACEA.*

65. *communis*,   Porpoise. Black without patches above ; tail black, flippers black ; dorsal low.

The Porpoise, that is the pig-fish, is our best-known dolphin, and is frequently seen and caught off our coasts, and occasionally up several of our largest rivers. It has a short, broad, tapering snout, beyond which the lower jaw slightly projects. In each jaw all along there are from sixteen to twenty-six pairs of small, spatulate teeth, which broaden from the narrow bases by which they rise from the gum. The low dorsal fin begins in the centre of the back and is triangular in shape, and frequently has a row of tubercles on its straight fore-edge ; its height is less than its base. The flippers are ovate in shape and twice as long as the dorsal is high, being about a seventh of the total length of the body, which is under six feet. The white of the

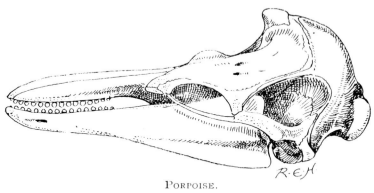

PORPOISE.
(*Phocæna communis.*)

underparts does not extend on to the flippers, the tail or, in some cases, the lower jaw. The porpoise is generally caught in nets into which it blunders in pursuit of the fishes on which it feeds.

Physeter.   Plate xxii.   *CETACEA.*

59.   *macrocephalus*, SPERM WHALE.   Head massive, measuring a third of total length, truncated in front ; lower jaw long, narrow, and toothed.

The Sperm Whale is a rare visitor whose visits to Britain, dead or alive, are becoming rarer. The huge, clumsy head contains the largest skull extant—a skull which is not symmetrical, the right jaw being larger than the left, and the right nasal being absent. In the upper jaw the teeth are rudimentary and embedded in the gum, but there are from twenty to twenty-five pairs in the lower jaw, which is long and narrow, with the branches united for more than half their length. The throat is expansible and has two grooves. The eye is slightly above the angle of the mouth. The blow-hole—only one as in all the toothed whales—is the shape of a violin sound-hole, and placed on the left side near the front of the muzzle, so that the jet is more forward than upright, and by the angle of the spout the Sperm Whale can be identified at a distance. The flippers are a tenth of the total length, and obliquely truncated ; the back fin is represented by a series of low humps ; the tail is deeply cleft, and the flukes, as in many other whales, are alternate, like the blades of a screw propeller. The length over all is sixty feet or less, the female being much smaller than the male. The colour is black above shading into grey below. The Sperm Whale, huge as it is, can leap clear out of the water. It feeds to a large extent on fishes, ranging from the smallest up to albacores and bonitos, but its main diet consists of squids and cuttles.   Ambergris, a biliary concretion formed in the intestine, was first identified as coming from this whale by the numerous beaks of cephalopods it contains.   Spermaceti is not

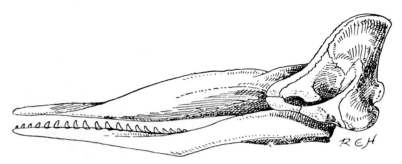

SPERM WHALE.
(*Physeter macrocephalus.*)

really *sperma ceti*—the Latin for sperm of the whale—but the oil within the vast cavity above the skull.   Unlike ambergris, it is not peculiar to this species, that from the head of the bottle _ _ _ ə being just as good.

Plecotus.   Plate i.   *CHIROPTERA.*

   3.   *auritus,*   LONG-EARED BAT.   Ears united and about as long as the forearm, the outer edges ending in a wart at the angle of the mouth.

   The Long-eared Bat has a very flat head, with the nostrils placed in front of curved grooves on the upper surface of its hairy muzzle. There is a wart over each eye, the eyes being small.   The feet are

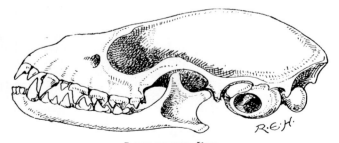

LONG-EARED BAT.
(*Plecotus auritus.*)

slender, and the wing membrane starts from the base of the toes. It has thirty-six teeth in all, of which the lower premolars number three on each side.   In colour it is pale brown above and whitish beneath, but darker when young. In length its head and body measure about one inch and three quarters, its tail is a trifle less, its ear and forearm are about an inch and a half. Its range includes Ireland and Scotland, and extends to the Himalaya. This species has the capricious flight of the common bat, but is generally met with in open country, and seldom near trees.

Putorius. Plate vi. *CARNIVORA.*

24. *fœtidus,*   POLECAT. Tail blackish throughout; colour dark grizzly brown, under fur buff; length over twelve inches.

25. *erminea,*   STOAT. Tip of tail black; colour reddish brown above, yellowish white of under parts extending up the sides; winter coat wholly or partially white.

26 *hibernicus,*   IRISH STOAT. Tip of tail black; colour reddish brown above, white of the underparts not extending up the sides; winter coat not white.

27. *vulgaris,*   WEASEL. Tip of tail reddish brown; colour reddish brown above, white below; length under eight inches.

This genus has three incisors, one canine, and three premolars in each jaw, and one molar in the upper jaw and two in the lower. In other words, it has a premolar less in each jaw than *Mustela.* There is no inner cusp to the lower flesh tooth, the flesh teeth being the last upper premolar and the lower molar. All the species have long, slender, supple bodies, with the tail less than half the length of the head and body combined. The limbs are short, and the claws semi-retractile.

At all seasons there is an offensive odour about the Polecat which is unmistakable. As a general rule the coat is a grizzly blackish brown, owing to the whitish under-fur showing through the long thin covering of dark hairs from which the artists' brushes are

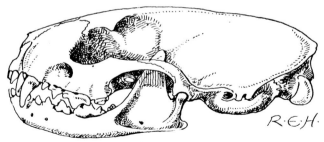

POLECAT.
(*Putorius fœtidus.*)

made. There is always a certain amount of white near the ears and mouth, but in summer the coarse outer coat is comparatively thick, so that the general colour is nearly black; in winter it is much paler. The head is twice as long as it is high, the neck thick, the muzzle rather rounded, with the upper canines prominent ; the ears are short and sub-angular ; the dark brown eyes are small and fierce in expression, and the sharp strong teeth tell the same tale of ferocity. The skull is ridged and compact, particularly in the "hob" or male, the female being known as the "jill," as in the case of the Ferret, which is a domesticated variety of this species ; in fact, the Polecat is sometimes known as the Ferret, though oftener as the Black Ferret or Fitchet. It is nocturnal in habits, and rarely takes to the trees, but hunts on the ground, kills more than it can eat, and generally carrying the prey to its lair to feed on it undisturbed. It will kill birds of all sorts, even geese and turkeys, and suck eggs, large or small, and it is particularly partial to rabbits and leverets, and has been seen to swim and dive in capturing eels and other fishes. In summer it shelters in holes and among rocks ; in winter it seems to prefer outhouses and ruins. The young, four to six in a litter, are born about May. In length the Polecat measures a little under two feet over all, the tail in large specimens being about seven.inches. It ranges over Central and Northern Europe, and used to be fairly common in the wilder parts of Ireland, Scotland, and England, but has been almost exterminated by gamekeepers.

In winter, when the Stoat is brought within the snow-line, it changes its coat to white, and becomes the Ermine. In districts where the snow does not linger long on the ground it becomes more or less white, but very seldom does it lose the black tip to its tail. In summer it is reddish brown on the back, the dark colour extend-ing half way down the sides, and there joining the sulphury white of the under parts ; and in winter, when the white spreads over the whole body, there is more or less of a sulphury tinge about it, especially at the beginning of the black brush. In length, the head and body range from about nine to over ten inches, the tail being rather less than half as long. The female is less in size and darker in colour than her mate, and, when old, has white markings on her dark fur even in July. The Stoat, as a rule, lives in stony places, a favourite haunt being a rough stone wall, but is not particular, and the nest of leaves and moss, with the five young, may be found in a rabbit burrow, or a hole in a hedge bank. "That vermin the ermine" is out on the prowl by day as well as by night, can climb and swim as well as it can run and leap, and includes every British rodent in its bill of fare. Squirrels, mice, rats, voles, hares, and rabbits all pay toll to it, as also do poultry and game birds in a smaller degree. It ranges all round the northern hemisphere, and in Russia and Canada is of commercial value for its fur. Like the Polecat, the male is a "hob" and the female a "jill."

The Irish Stoat is of the same habits and the same size, but differs in colour, the light fulvous brown above, instead of ending half way down the sides, extending on to the abdomen, and there joining the narrow white area which runs from the chest between the legs to the tail. In short, the colour plan is that of the Weasel ; the size that of the Stoat. And the colour is the same all the year round, there being no turning to white in Ireland, perhaps because the snow is not sufficiently frequent or lasting to render it necessary. But as the species is not found out of Ireland, it is impossible to say.

The Weasel is much the smallest of the four species, the head and body rarely measuring over eight inches, and the short, round, pointed tail not exceeding two inches and a half. The head is three times as long as it is high, the length being about an inch and three-quarters. The Weasel is duller in appearance than the Stoat, owing to the white being confined to the throat and abdomen, the rich cinnamon brown of the back extending all over the sides. In the extreme north the Weasel turns white like the Stoat; but with us, even in the North of Scotland, it does not get beyond the spotted stage. When it does turn white, it always retains the reddish brown tip to the tail. The Weasel hunts by day and night; in fact, it is proverbially difficult to catch one asleep, and when awake he is always on the alert. Arching his long, supple body as he runs, he will systematically work across every portion of a field or hillside in pursuit of his prey, and will climb and swim, and leap into the air almost a yard from the ground rather than lose it. He chiefly feeds on rats, mice, and voles, and where they are found he is found; when they fail, or perhaps, by way of a change—but never for long —he takes to small birds, the depredations amongst game, ground game, and poultry, for which he often gets credit, being in most cases chargeable to the Stoat. The female is an inch or more smaller than the male. The nest is a pile of dried leaves, herbage, and moss, in a hole in the ground or a hollow tree. There are six or fewer young at a time, and two or three litters a year. The female will carry her young, one at a time, in her mouth out of danger, as will the male, so that mother and father have been observed removing the family in three journeys together in this fashion. No animal makes a better fight for its young than the Weasel. It ranges round the northern hemisphere, and though fairly common north and south of the Tweed, is unknown in Ireland, where its name has been given to the native Stoat, an alias productive of even more confusion than in England, where there is less excuse owing to both species existing in the same localities.

Rhinolophus.   Plate i.   *CHIROPTERA.*

 1. *ferrum-equinum*, GREATER HORSE-SHOE BAT. Head and body exceeding two inches; no gap between upper canines and premolars, second lower premolar external to line of teeth.

 2. *hipposiderus*, LESSER HORSE-SHOE BAT. Head and body less than two inches; a gap between upper canines and premolars, second lower premolar in the angle between the other teeth.

These Horse-shoe Bats are so-called from the outgrowth round the nostrils, known as the nose-leaf, which is in three portions, of which the outermost is in the form of a small horse-shoe. They have no tragus or inner earlet, though they have an anti-tragus, or secondary earlet.   The wing membrane starts from the ankles, and the tip of the tail projects beyond it.

In the Greater Horse-shoe the ears are very pointed, and shorter than the head.   In colour it is greyish-brown above, and greyish-white below.   In length its head measures an inch, its body rather more than an inch and a quarter, its tail an inch and a half, and its

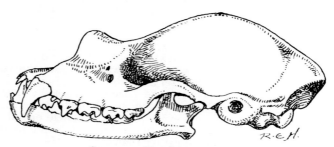

GREATER HORSE-SHOE BAT.
(*Rhinolophus ferrum-equinum.*)

fore-arm two inches and a quarter.   Like the other Horse-shoe Bat, it has two joints in its first hind-toe, and three in the others. It is a tree-haunting species, confined to the South of England, and ranging thence to Japan and South Africa.

In the Lesser Horse-shoe Bat the ears are pointed and nearly as long as the head, and have the outer edge hollowed out near the tip.   There is a well-marked notch at the junction with the secondary earlet.   The nose-leaf is toothed along its outer margin.   As in the preceding species, there is a vertical groove in the lower lip.   In colour it is pale brown above, lighter and more greyish below.   The head and body measure about an inch and a half, the tail is a little over an inch, the fore-arm an inch and a half.   This Bat ranges from Ireland, through the South of England, across Europe down into Africa, but has not been found south of the Equator.

Sciurus.   Plate x.   *RODENTIA.*

35.   *vulgaris,*   SQUIRREL.   Colour brownish red and reddish grey ; tail large and bushy.

The Squirrel is well known for his rich brownish red coat and his bushy tail curled up along his back, but his coat in winter is very grey—the colder the climate the greyer he gets—and his tail is always held straight when he runs or swims, and spread out with his legs when he leaps from branch to branch, in a way that suggests his flying relatives of the tropics.   He is always white below, from the throat downwards, and has tufts to his ears during the first six months of the year.   He measures about sixteen inches over all, rather less than half of this being taken up by the tail ; the female being always of smaller build and lighter colour. The eyes and ears are large. The short, rounded skull is noteworthy for its broad frontals, and long postorbital processes. There are no canine teeth, and only one pair of incisors in each jaw ; in the upper jaw are two premolars, one of which is diminutive and soon lost, and three molars ; and in the lower set are one premolar and three molars. In the hand are four digits, and a rudimentary thumb, which is almost opposable ; and in the foot are five toes, all, like the fingers, with long, sharp claws with which he clings to the bark as he runs up the trees. He is always found in woods, generally where beeches, oaks, and hazels are plentiful, for he feeds on beech mast, acorns, nuts, young shoots, fungi, eggs, insects, and sundries. In eating a nut he scrapes off the small end with his teeth as he

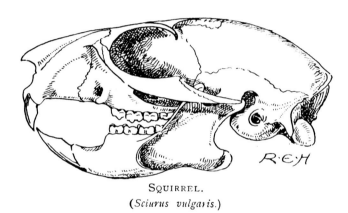

SQUIRREL.
(*Sciurus vulgaris.*)

holds it in his hands, splits the shell in two as a man might do with a knife, and, before he eats the kernel, carefully removes the skin. He lays up stores of food for the winter, and is up and about when-ever the weather is mild or sunny, so that he can hardly be said to hibernate. He pairs for life, and the young, from three to seven in number, are born blind in a nest or "drey," fairly well made of leaves, fibres, and moss, in a fork of a tree or a hole in the stem. Few would suppose that he is the "camel" of whose hair the paint-brushes are made. He lives in suitable localities all over the country, even in Ireland, and ranges thence as far east as Japan, and as far south as the North of Italy.

Sorex. Plate iv. *INSECTIVORA.*

18. *vulgaris,*   COMMON SHREW. Over two inches and a half in length exclusive of tail ; third upper incisor not longer than adjoining tooth.

19. *minutus,*   LESSER SHREW.   Under two inches and a half in
length exclusive of tail; third upper incisor longer
than adjoining tooth.

The teeth of the Shrews, minute as they are, afford the best
means of identification.   To begin with, they are tipped with
reddish brown, and the front pair in each jaw are longer than the
others, and point forwards, those in the upper series being curved.
In each half of the upper jaw there are ten teeth, and in the lower
there are only six or seven, but opinions differ as to how
they should be named.   All agree that there are three molars
in each jaw, and three premolars in the upper jaw and one
in the lower; but the other upper four teeth are classed by
some as incisors, and by some as three incisors and a canine,
the lower jaw having two or three incisors only, the canine
being absent.   Whatever the upper fourth tooth may be, it is very
useful for distinguishing between the two British examples, the
smaller species having it clearly shorter than the tooth alongside.
Both Shrews have long, narrow, pointed snouts, small, rounded
ears, that only just project above the fur, and hairy tails that are
shorter than the head and body, rather square in section, and about
the same thickness for most of their length.

The Common Shrew is fulvous grey above, paler below.   Its
head and body measure about three inches, the tail being half as long.
It is nocturnal in habit, and feeds on worms and snails, as well as

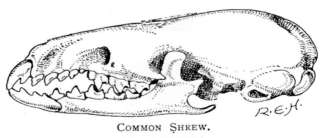

COMMON SHREW.
(*Sorex vulgaris.*)

insects.   The young, from five to ten in a litter, are born in a neat
covered nest, with the entrance at the side.   The species is found
all round the northern hemisphere, except in Ireland and the
Hebrides.

The Lesser Shrew is proportionately shorter in the fore limbs,
besides being smaller in size, the head and body never exceeding
two inches in length, the tail being an inch and a quarter.   This is
for a full-sized female, the male being smaller still.   In fact, the
Lesser Shrew is the smallest British mammal; the largest, Sibbald's
Rorqual, being some three hundred and fifty times as long.   In
colour, it is rather darker than the common species.   It ranges

eastwards from Ireland and the Hebrides to Saghalien; and, like the Common Shrew, feeds mainly on insect larvæ, worms, and small molluscs, brings forth its young in a domed nest, and sleeps through the winter in some hole in the ground.

Synotus. Plate i. *CHIROPTERA.*

4. *barbastellus,* BARBASTELLE. Ears large and united, and enclosing the eyes by reaching half-way down between them and the tip of the muzzle.

In the Barbastelle the nostrils open on the top of the bare muzzle, and a groove passes down from each so as to thicken the upper lip in the middle. There are thirty-four teeth in all, of which the lower premolars number two on each side. The feet are slender, the toes long, being half the length of the foot, and the wing membrane starts from the base of the toes. The tail, which is an inch and

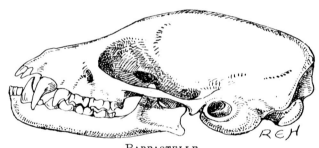

BARBASTELLE.
(*Synotus barbastellus.*)

three-quarters long, slightly projects beyond the membrane. The head and body are as long as the tail. In colour the Barbastelle is black above and below, with a tendency to greyish; but occasionally specimens are met with much lighter in colouration, including the inevitable albino. It has not yet been recorded from Ireland or Scotland, but ranges from the North of England to Northern Africa, and well into Asia north of the Himalaya.

Talpa. Plate iv. *INSECTIVORA.*

17. *europæa,* MOLE. No external ears; eyes hidden in fur; feet not webbed.

The Mole bores with its muscular muzzle, which is strengthened by a special bone, and, with the powerful arms, clears the way as the legs drive it along. From the tip of the nose to the last of the ribs the shape is that of a flattened cone, practically unbroken by shoulders owing to the lengthened presternum bringing the clavicle against the side of the neck, and enabling the hand to begin its outward sweep from the very end of the jaw. The broad, strong hand is turned outwards instead of downwards, and the immense development of the radial sesamoid, otherwise the falciform bone, seems to give it six fingers instead of five. The milk teeth are forty-four in number—three incisors, a canine, four premolars, and three molars in the half of each jaw—but in the permanent set a premolar is missing, so that there are only forty. The forward upper incisors are like chisels, and slightly larger than the second pair, the upper canine is large, the last upper premolar has no internal basal process, and the molars are uniform in shape, with well-defined zigzag cusps. The mole is not quite blind; the eyes, though hidden in the fur, being usable, but small—so small that in the skull the orbits are almost indistinguishable. There are no external ears. The total length reaches seven inches, of which the tail measures nearly an inch and a half, being as long as the head. The colour ranges from black to buff, the fur being vertical, short and velvety, so as to offer no hindrance to movement backwards or forwards in close quarters underground; in fact, the animal is

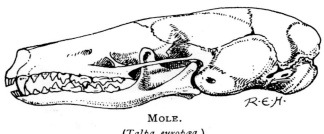

MOLE.

(*Talpa europæa.*)

obviously adapted in all respects for its peculiar life. As is well known, its tunnels are of great length and complicated plan, one of them always communicating with water—a pond or a stream, or even downwards as a sort of well—for the mole is almost as thirsty as it is hungry, and it is very hungry, not to say voracious, as might be expected from the immense amount of navvy work it has to do. It feeds upon worms and larvæ, and does about as much good as harm to the farmer and gardener, but the hills it makes are inconvenient and unsightly, and the plants it kills by driving its galleries too close to the roots are many, so that it is remorselessly sought after. It is easily caught by traps in its "runs," and is easily killed, for a tap on the nose is as fatal to it as to a badger. The males are more numerous than the females; the young average four to a birth, and they are born in a nest of leaves and rootlets, discoverable, as a rule, under some "hill" of larger dimensions than the rest. The Mole can swim as well as run and tunnel. Its forty-four teeth are an interesting survival of a very early stage in its development, and its tiny eyes prove that it took to finding its livelihood underground at a comparatively recent period. It is not found in Ireland, but is widely distributed throughout England and Scotland up to Caith-ness, and ranges eastwards from Anglesey to Japan.

Tursiops. Plate xxvi. *CETACEA.*

72. *tursio,*   BOTTLE-NOSE DOLPHIN. Forehead rounded; beak broad, depressed, and gently tapering; lower jaw longer than upper.

This rare visitor to our British estuaries is fairly common in the Western Atlantic. In colour it is generally dark bluish grey above, shading into white below, but seems to vary down to black with a white abdominal streak. The head is large and rounded, the whitish beak projecting from it with hardly any interruption of the curve. The beak is rather more than half as long as the skull. The gape is curved, and the lower jaw is the longer. There

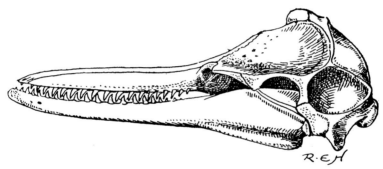

BOTTLE-NOSE DOLPHIN.
(*Tursiops tursio.*)

are twenty-two or twenty-three pairs of teeth, and the palate is not grooved. The eye is large and the eyelids very mobile. The dorsal fin is broad and high, and the flippers long and falcate. The length is twelve feet or less. There are sixty-four or sixty-five vertebræ and twelve or thirteen ribs, of which five are double-headed. In spring all ages and sexes are found together, but later on they sort themselves out, and some of the shoals have been found to consist entirely of old males.

Vespertilio. Plate iii. *CHIROPTERA.*

Feet long—

10. *dasycneme,*   ROUGH-LEGGED BAT. Earlet not pointed but rounded ; ears shorter than head.

11. *daubentoni,*   DAUBENTON'S BAT. Earlet pointed ; ears as long as head.

Feet short—

12. *nattereri,*   REDDISH-GREY BAT. Earlet curving outwards ; membrane between legs fringed with long hairs.

13. *bechsteini,*   BECHSTEIN'S BAT. Earlet curving outwards ; membrane between legs without hairs.

14. *murinus,*   MOUSE-COLOURED BAT.   Earlet straight ; no long hairs on upper lip.

15. *mystacinus,*   WHISKERED BAT.   Earlet straight ; long hairs on upper lip.

In this genus the outer edge of the ear begins in a line with the inner margin of the earlet ; the ears are generally as long as, or longer, than the head, and are narrow and thin ; the earlet is straight or curved outwards ; the muzzle is narrow and hairy in front of the eyes, and has no glandular swellings. The first premolar is well developed, instead of being small or absent, and there are on each side of the upper jaw two incisors, one canine, three premolars, and three molars, the first and second premolars being smaller than the third. The nostrils are simple, and the nasal apertures crescentic in shape. The wing-membrane starts from the base of the toes or thereabouts.

The Rough-legged Bat has short ears, which, in both margins, are straight in the lower third and become convex towards the tip ; the earlet has the inner margin concave and the outer margin convex. The feet are long, and there is a large claw on the thumb. The face is not very hairy. In colour this species is brown, the hairs above having drab tips, those below having white tips. The head and body measure nearly two inches and a half ; the tail measures two inches. The Rough-legged Bat ranges through temperate Asia into Europe, and is said to occasionally visit the south of England, though only one specimen has found its way into our records.

Daubenton's Bat has ears long enough to reach the tip of its nose, and they are concave in the upper third of their outer margins. The earlet is half as long as the ears, the end being straight and not curved outwards, and there is a rounded lobe just above the base. The face is bare, with a few hairs in front of the ears. The colour is brown above and whitish below, where the tips of the dark brown hairs become longer and paler. In length its head and body do not quite reach two inches, and the tail is a quarter-inch less. The wing-spread is about nine inches. Though not a common species, it is widely distributed over the three kingdoms, and thence ranges into Asia as far as Tennasserim, being generally noticed over water, skimming the surface in chase of the insects on which it feeds.

The Reddish-Grey Bat has the ears longer than the head, and they are semi-transparent, and marked with glandular papillæ. The earlet is long, curving outwards and sharply pointed. The fringe of stiff hairs on the membrane between the legs is very noticeable. The fur is long and thick, dark brown above, and whitish below, tipped with reddish on the upper parts, and with white on the lower, the white under-surface rendering the species easily recognisable when in flight. The head and body measure an inch and three-quarters ; the tail is about as long. The fore-arm measures an inch and a half, and the wing-spread is eleven inches. This Bat is known all over Europe north of the Alps and west of the Urals.

and, with us, ranges into Ireland, and at least as far north as Argyleshire, its resting-places being never in trees, but always in buildings or caverns.

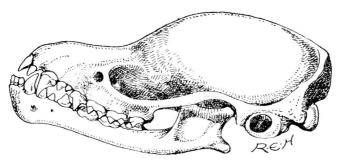

REDDISH-GREY BAT.
(*Vespertilio nattereri.*)

Bechstein's Bat has longer ears and a shorter tail than the preceding, the ears being much longer than the head, and the tail being shorter than the head and body. The membrane connecting the legs is not fringed with hairs. On the upper surface the dark brown hairs have reddish tips, on the under parts the tips are ashy. The head and body measure two inches, the tail is half an inch shorter, the ear is an inch in length, and the fore-arm measures two inches. This species is confined to Europe north of the Alps, and in the British Isles, up to the present, has only been captured in Hampshire.

The Mouse-coloured Bat has large blunt ears, a little longer than the head, and a straight earlet, with rather a sharp point. The muzzle is conical, and the nostrils are close together. The wing-membrane rises from slightly above the base of the toes; the membrane between the legs is hairy on the upper surface, but not fringed, and the tail just projects beyond its edge. The head and body measure two inches and three-quarters; the tail is a trifle over two inches in length, the fore-arm over two inches and a half, and the third digit measures four inches. This is the largest British Bat, its wing-spread reaching fifteen inches. It is mouse-coloured above and greyer below, the hairs being all dark in their lower portions. Only a few examples of this large species are recorded as British, and they seem to have been caught in the garden of the British Museum, but there is no reason why it should not cross the Channel. It is common all over the Continent, and ranges into India and Abyssinia.

The Whiskered Bat is recognisable at once by its moustache and by its wing-membrane starting from the base of its outer toe. The ears are as long as the head, and the earlet is long and straight, with a rounded lobe at the base of the outer margin.   In colour this Bat is pale brown above and ashy below, the hairs being all blackish brown with paler tips.   The head and body are an inch and a half long, the head, like the ear, measuring only half an inch ; the tail is almost as long as the head and body, and longer than the forearm, which measures only an inch and a quarter, though the wing-spread extends to between eight and nine. It ranges from Ireland across England right away to Pekin and as far south as the Sahara. It is a solitary species, appearing early after sundown, frequently noticed flying low over water, and found hibernating in hollow trees, old buildings, and chalk caves.

Vesperugo.   Plate ii.   *CHIROPTERA.*

Wing-membrane rising from base of toes—

5.   *serotinus,*   SEROTINE.   Dark brown ; membrane near spur narrow ; head and body over two inches.

9.   *pipistrellus,*   PIPISTRELLE.   Reddish brown ; membrane near spur broad ; head and body under two inches.

6.   *discolor,*   PARTI-COLOURED BAT.   Brown and white ; membrane near spur broad and distinct ; lower outer incisors half as thick as upper outer incisors ; head and body measuring two inches.

Wing-membrane rising from ankle—

7.   *noctula,*   NOCTULE.   Light brown, hairs paler at base ; membrane near spur narrow and indistinct ; lower outer incisors half as thick as upper incisors.

8.   *leisleri,*   HAIRY-ARMED BAT.   Light brown, hairs darker at base ; membrane near spur narrow and indistinct ; lower outer incisors of similar thickness to upper outer incisors.

In this genus the outer edge of the ear begins near the angle of the mouth, the ears are generally shorter than the head, and triangular or rhomboidal in outline, the earlet is curved inwards or straight, and the muzzle is broad and nearly bare in front of the eyes, with conspicuous glandular prominences.   The first premolar is absent or small, and there are on each side of each jaw two incisors, one canine, one or two premolars, and three molars, making twenty-eight or thirty-two teeth in all, the upper incisors being bifid and separated by a gap from the canines.   There is no lobe on the lower lip near the angle of the mouth.

The Serotine has ears rather shorter than its head, with their outer edge straight or slightly hollowed.   On the face the fur is short, on the upper lip there is a fringe of straight hairs, and on the chin are longish hairs which radiate from a wart.   On the upper parts the colour is dark brown, the brown hairs having pale tips, below the general colour ranges from pale brown to buff.   The head and body measure about two inches and three quarters, the tail two inches, and the fore-arm two and a quarter.   The Serotine is confined to the south of England amongst us, but is remarkable for its wide distribution over Europe, Asia, Central Africa, and Northern America, where it ranges from Winnipeg to Guatemala under the name of the Carolina Bat.

The Parti-coloured Bat has ears about half as long as the face, the inner margin being convex and the outer ending in a wart at the angle of the mouth. The muzzle is not pointed, though the upper lip slightly projects, and the glandular prominences are not conspicuously large. The tail measures an inch and three-quarters in length, the head and body a quarter of an inch more. The characteristic colour is due to the dark brown hairs of the coat having long white tips, which are of a yellowish tinge on the upper parts and ashy on the under parts. This Bat ranges through Europe to Turkestan, mostly in mountainous districts, but the only unmistakable evidence of its occurrence in this country is afforded by the specimen at South Kensington.

In the Noctule the ears are nearly as broad as long, and when pulled down over the face reach a little below the eyes. They are rather thick and are convex on both sides, the convexity on the inner side ending in a straight run to the tip. The head is broad, the labial prominences large, and the nostrils wide apart with a hollow space between. The thumb is short, with a short, sharp claw ; the feet are thick, the toes short, and the tip of the tail slightly projects beyond the membrane between the legs. The Noctule sleeps with the tail between the legs instead of curving it backwards and

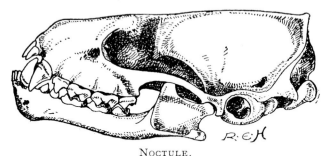

NOCTULE.
(*Vesperugo noctula.*)

upwards. In colour it is yellowish or reddish brown, lighter below, the hairs on the upper part being paler at the base than at the tip. It is a large bat, its wing-spread being thirteen or fourteen inches, its head and body measuring three inches and its tail about two. From its flying high Gilbert White concluded that it was "supported by some sorts of high-flying gnats, scarabs, or phælænæ," which is true, as it feeds mainly on beetles which fly high, and in quest of them the Noctule is generally found in the neighbourhood of trees. It ranges from the north of England to Japan, South Africa, and the Malay Archipelago.

F

The Hairy-armed Bat is a small edition of the Noctule, with the fringe of hair down the under-side of the fore-arm rather more marked, and the lower incisor teeth neatly arranged instead of crowded together. In colour it is dark brown both above and below, but the hairs on the upper surface are tipped with yellowish, while those below are tipped with light brown. The head and body measure just over two inches and a quarter, the tail about an inch and three-quarters. It flies at all heights, and ranges from Ireland, through England, across Europe into Asia north of the Himalaya.

The Pipistrelle is the smallest and commonest of British bats. Its ears are broadly triangular, rounded at the tips, like the earlets, with their outer edge ending in a large lobe. The head and face are rather hairy, the muzzle short, the glandular prominences conspicuous, and the nostrils opening forwards. In colour it is rufous brown, the hairs above being black on the basal half, those below having ashy tips. The head and body measure under an inch and three quarters, and the tail under an inch and a half. The ear is about half an inch long, the fore-arm measures an inch and a quarter, and the characteristically long fifth digit reaches an inch and a half. The wing-spread is between eight and nine inches. The feet are small, with a broad lobe of membrane behind the spur. It feeds mainly on gnats and flies, and suits its flight to capture them—buoyant, brisk, capricious, up and down, high as the tree-tops, low as within a foot of the water—but averaging on calm evenings about three men's lengths from the ground. It seems as fearless of man as the sparrow, and is found in many a town where there are open spaces large enough for it to hunt over from sunset to sunrise. It is found all over England, Ireland, and Scotland, and it ranges from the Outer Hebrides, across Europe, into Northern Africa, and as far south-east in Asia as the Vale of Kashmir. Like the other bats it sleeps during the winter, but it is hardier and earlier, appearing in March and not retiring until November, and it has been known to wake up and take advantage of an occasional warm day in January and February.

Vulpes.   Plate v.   *CARNIVORA.*

   22. *vulgaris,*   Fox.   Tail bushy;   claws short, blunt, and not retractile.

The Fox is generally reddish-brown above and white and pale grey below, with black on the back of the ears and the front of the feet, whitish brows, and a white tip to the long bushy tail; but the colouration varies a good deal, the gaunt " Hill Fox," or " Greyhound Fox," of Scotland and the Border uplands—like the big, thick-set " Mastiff Fox," and the short-legged " Terrier Fox "— being very grey. Sometimes the tail is tipped with black, as in the " Cur Fox," occasionally with grey, and a certain Warwickshire fox is on record which, like the " Welsh Fox," had the underparts blackish instead of white. The head is broad, the muzzle long and pointed, the ears large and erect, and the eyes, which have elliptical pupils, are singularly bright and intelligent. There are forty-two teeth, consisting of three incisors (i), a canine (c), and four premolars (p.m), in each jaw, and two molars in the upper jaw, and three in the lower. The upper carnassial is the fourth premolar, and it has two lobes to the outer blade ; the lower carnassial is the first molar (m), and it has a broad heel at the hinder end, and a small cusp on the inner side. The upper molars are triangular ; of the lower molars the third is very small, and has a roundish crown and but one root. In short, the teeth are those of a dog, and the tongue is smooth like a dog's, the noteworthy differences in the skull being the slightly upward curve of the postorbital process of the frontal, the concavity of its upper surface, and the absence of a frontal sinus. And, like a dog, the fox will eat almost

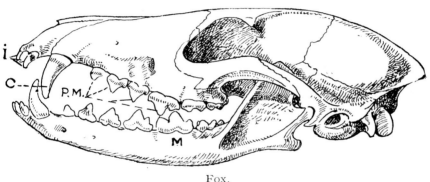

Fox.
(*Vulpes vulgaris.*)

anything animal from a lamb to an insect or the molluscs and crustaceans on the seashore, besides a good many vegetable things, including, of course, the proverbial grapes when it can get them. Unlike the dogs, the female, or " vixen " as she is called, has but six teats. The fox stands about fourteen inches at the withers, and averages over three feet over all, including the " brush " or tail, which is a third as long as the head and body together. It lives as a rule in pairs, not always in a burrow, but when it does the " earth " consists of a central den with more than one exit, the slope of which is downwards and upwards. The prey. mainly rabbits and mice, is hunted by night, but foxes have been frequently noticed sunning themselves in the day-time. The young, or " cubs," from four to six in number, begin to hunt with their mother when three months old ; when about half that age they play about in front of the burrow, barking in a small way for food. The Fox can not only run long distances, but can swim and climb, and is notorious for his general resourcefulness ; but even this would not have saved him being driven to the farthest north like the wild cat, or wiped off the British list altogether, had it not been for the sport he affords, which means so many things besides the mere capture of his brush.   It is only in hunting districts, however, that he is preserved to run for his life ; in other parts the keepers trap him for his depredations amongst the game. He is met with in all three kingdoms, and ranges all round the northern hemisphere, for the American red fox, cross fox, and silver fox, but not the kit fox, grey fox, or Arctic fox, are now generally held to be mere varieties of the European form.

Ziphius.   Plate xxiii.   *CETACEA*.

62. *cavirostris*,   CUVIER'S WHALE.   A pair of teeth at outer end of lower jaw.

Of this rare, widely-distributed whale, only one example is as yet on record as having visited British waters, and that one got stranded in the Shetlands.   The beak is triangular, rather long, and gradually tapering.   At the outer end of the lower jaw are two prominent teeth, and in the upper jaw are several small teeth hidden in the gums and evidently of no use.   The throat has one

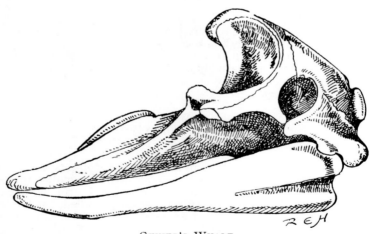

CUVIER'S WHALE.
(*Ziphius cavirostris.*)

groove on each side ; the blow-hole is crescentic ; the flippers are angular on the forward edge ; the dorsal is small and placed well back, and the tail is deeply cleft.   In colour this whale is black above and white below, and it is under thirty feet in length and has forty-nine vertebræ, of which only the first three are united. The name *Ziphius* is from the sword-like nature of the beak.

CHAPTER V.

THE BRITISH MAMMALS PAST AND PRESENT.

———————◆———————

IN our list of British mammals one is subterranean, five are closely preserved, three are more or less preserved, twenty-seven live in the water, and the remaining twenty-six are either nocturnal or crepuscular—that is to say, only those survive that man cannot get at. Of these, thirty-eight may be described as common, but none of them so all over the country, twenty-seven are decidedly rare, and seven owe their place in the list to their having been met with on one occasion only.

This suggests the question as to what is a British animal, the reply being that it is one that is not recorded as having been introduced into this country, and has had the misfortune to be captured to prove its occurrence and its identity. That it has drifted here accidentally, that is, a mere straggler, perhaps to our remotest islands, makes no difference; to require it to have been born within our boundaries is evidently too severe a test; neither need it have resided here for any length of time; all that is required is for it to be captured and by its death obtain its naturalisation.

Our list may not satisfy everyone, but it is as we found it. Two species in particular may be singled out for objection. The Fallow Deer is stated, with much probability, to have been introduced by the Romans, and doubts have been cast by some on the origin of our Park Cattle, which are said to be feral—that is, descended from domesticated species run wild—in just the same way as the wild goats of Mull and Killarney, or the Four-horned Sheep of St. Kilda and the Hebrides which, though wild now, are known to have come from the sheep that found their way ashore from the wrecks of some of the vessels of the Spanish Armada.

As with the present so with the past, every animal that we find has died here we claim as British, and although in this book we are concerned with existing species now in this area, we can hardly omit mentioning those still existent elsewhere which used to live here, as well as those which have become extinct throughout the world. Including these, we shall have a very long list, which, of necessity, will become longer as the rocks yield up their records, and will never be really complete. As we have it here, it runs to two hundred and seventy-five species, of which seventy-two are still with us, thirty-four are existent elsewhere, and one hundred and sixty-nine have died out.

This enlarged British list takes us back to the times when there was no Britain, for the geological changes have been great. Our first amphibian dates from the Lower Carboniferous, our first reptile from the Permian, our first mammal only from the Rhætics, when the sea broke into the Triassic lake which extended from what is now the Continent, up the middle of England, into the north-east of Ireland, and perhaps beyond.   The sea extended the boundaries of the lake, much as the Black Sea might do if it broke into the sinking Caspian, and by the continued subsidence became deep enough for the deposition of the Lias, and with many changes of level and other conditions received on its bed that wonderful series of fossiliferous clays and limestones we know as the Oolites ; the dark-coloured clays, like the Lias, being probably due to the denudation of the surrounding carboniferous country, the limestone forming when the water cleared, and ceasing when each new arrival of clay destroyed its builders. Eventually upheaval towards the north reduced the sea to the smaller area in which the Portlandian series was formed, and further upheaval left it as the lake, or series of lagoons, whose presence we trace in the alternate freshwater, marine, and brackish fauna of the Purbecks.

When the Cretaceous period began, the land-surface extended far westward and northward into the Atlantic, and the Purbeck lagoons had become freshwater lakes which widened and united as subsidence set in, until the rivers that fed them ran through into the sea, which eventually spread over the entire area, and, after several vicissitudes, became deep enough for the formation of the chalk, when very little of what is now Britain remained above water as a scattered group of islets in an ocean which stretched from Asia over Europe, across the Atlantic into the southern states of North America.

After a long interval the chalk sea shallowed until much of its bed appeared above the waters and became dry land, there being, as usual, many outbursts of volcanic activity during this period of elevation.   The new land became clothed with luxuriant vegetation characteristic of a warm climate, and in time was peopled by quite a different fauna from that of the past.   Then the waters began to creep up in the south-east of what is now the British region, and in the bed of the rising sea the Thanet Sands were laid down ; and then, round the coast in the estuaries and lagoons, were formed the Woolwich and Reading beds, the elevation of the Wealden dome giving the island from the denudation of which came the materials for the Oldhaven pebble beach, which, as the sea-bed further sank, became the basement bed of the London Clay.   This familiar clay was evidently deposited in the deeper parts of a shallow sea from materials supplied by the surrounding rivers, one, or several, of which must have drained a considerable extent of country.

Towards the close of this clay period the sea again became shallow, either by silting up or gentle upheaval, and much of the London basin became a land surface in whose lakes and estuaries our Bagshots were formed from the denudation of the country to the north and west, and perhaps of the Wealden dome : while the Hampshire basin became a gulf in which the beds of that area were deposited from easterly-flowing rivers.   The continued subsidence brought in the sea from the west through the rocky high ground between Cornwall and Brittany, the eastern and western seas being kept apart for some time afterwards by the ridge in the south-east, through which they both subsequently made their way, so as to leave it as a promontory extending from England into Belgium.

Elevation followed, and again separated the seas and began the Oligocene period, in which all the British Isles were part of a land surface extending in a broad isthmus to the Continent, with the eastern sea over Holland and the western driven back and reduced to a shallow gulf between Cornwall and Brittany, ending in estuaries and lagoons in the Hampshire and Paris basins, in which the deposits thickened during the ensuing period of subsidence. Thus Britain, during the Oligocene epoch, was mainly dry land. and as such it remained during the formation of the Miocene rocks of southern and western France and elsewhere.

In the subsidence that occurred during early Pliocene times, the conspicuous events, as far as England is concerned, were the deposition of the Coralline Crag in the Suffolk gulf, which was the northernmost extension of the eastern sea, and the sinking of the southern portion of the country below the waves, causing the formation of the plane of denudation across the north and south downs, which was the first stage in the cutting down of the Valley of the Weald.

In Newer Pliocene days the movement of the land shut off the communication between the eastern sea and the Mediterranean, and opened up that between the Atlantic and the Arctic Ocean. In the south-east this uplift took the Coralline Crag up to water-level: the depression that closely followed taking it down again, throwing open communication between the Arctic Ocean, Atlantic, and North Sea, and leaving the British Isles as a triangular extension of France and Belgium, with a western boundary stretching from the Bay of Biscay beyond Ireland and the Hebrides up to the Orkneys. This subsidence was, however, not continuous, and the minor oscillations of level on the east coast are traceable in the formation of the Crags and Forest Bed. Even in those days Norfolk and Suffolk had their chain of "broads," evidently fed by a large river which, to judge by its gravels, received the drainage of the Ardennes and was in fact a branch of what is now the Rhine. There is good reason for supposing that during the deposition of the Walton Crag the southern subsidence was so general as to sever the peninsula for a time from the Continent: but whether this be so or not, it is clear that it was in Pliocene times that the Eocenes and Chalk were mainly eroded, and the direction given to many of the existing rivers, including the Thames and those of the Humber and the Wash.

Meanwhile a colder climate had been steadily advancing from the north, and in the next epoch, that of the Pleistocene, we find Britain under glacial conditions, with occasional warmer intervals as the ice receded to return again, until it left us almost entirely. To begin with, the land rose enough to join Scotland to Greenland, thus cutting off the extension of the Gulf Stream, and a vast amount of denudation took place, resulting in the deep excavation of many of our river valleys and the opening up of many of our limestone caves, while the glaciers were forming on the northern and western mountains. Then the land sank beneath the sea north of the line between the mouths of the Severn and the Thames; and Wales,

Ireland, Cumberland, and Scotland were represented by their mountain summits in the form of islands. Once again the sea-bed rose to sink again, and during this period of subsidence the waters finally cut their way through St. George's Channel and afterwards through the Straits of Dover, so as to leave the geography of the British Isles much as it is to-day.

From this rapid survey of our country's physical history since the first British mammal yet found dropped his teeth on the Rhætic mud, it is clear that, even considering the changes we have recorded —which are by no means all—the conditions of existence must have altered frequently and greatly. Throughout, the aquatic animals must have had by far the safer time of it, though, even they must at times have been shut in or perished from change of climate, or want of food, or the increase of enemies. But the land animals must either have been cut off at each submergence, or retired to a continent, when they could find one, there to breed and leave their descendants to venture on to the new land surface when vegetation had rendered it habitable.

That numbers of species must have passed away in this area and left no traces behind them seems to be almost inevitable. As the rocks were all deposited in water, the land animals, whose remains have been preserved, must either have met their deaths by drowning, or been washed into the water when dead, or swallowed by some aquatic carnivore who failed to digest their teeth and other hard parts. In any case they are not likely to be met with far from the shore, and hence it is that so few have been found in marine deposits. In the Secondary rocks they appear only in the estuarine beds of the Rhætics and Stonesfield Slate ; in the beds above the chalk they are more numerous because our Tertiary period was mainly one of lakes, lagoons, estuaries, and shallow seas ; and in the caves of the Pleistocene they owe their preservation, not to contemporaneous deposition, but mainly to the formation of stalagmite due to the percolation of water through the roof of the natural cavity they had chosen as their home for the dying.

Considering the preponderance of the chances against preservation the wonder is that our fossil animals should be so numerous. Evidently the faunas of the past were as rich as those of the present, though the classes were in different proportion. And the abundance of animal life agrees with the known luxuriance of vegetable life, for it is dependent on it, just as the vegetable life is dependent on the land surface as modified by denudation under the influences of climate. As examples of this interdependence of Nature we have the first appearance of the grasses in Cretaceous days followed by the incoming of the grass-feeding ungulates of the Eocene, then the arrival of the larger carnivores as soon as there was prey suitable for them, and finally the destruction of nearly all at the hands of omnivorous man, whom, for obvious reasons, we have not included in our list, though he was certainly here before our final separation from the continent, but perhaps in a form which many of his descendants would not care to recognise.

Some brief notes on our past faunas would seem to be necessary. The earliest British mammals as yet known are two species of

Microlestes from the Rhætic series, which comes, as we have said, between the Trias and Lias, and consequently almost at the base of the Secondary rocks. These are known by their teeth, one species, *M. moorei*, being from near Frome, the other, *M. rhæticus*, from Watchet. They are generally considered to be Marsupials, although, like the Wombats, the teeth have no continuations of the dentinal tubes traversing the enamel. It is inconceivable that they were the first mammals to die in this country, or even in what is now Somersetshire, but it is remarkable that no further traces of mammalian life have yet been discovered until we reach the Stonesfield Slate, none in the Lias, none in the Inferior Oolite, none until we arrive at the thin-bedded limestones at the base of the Great Oolite, which are called slates from being locally used for roofing purposes, and are unlike slates in every other particular.

These thin limestones have yielded five genera, all of them Marsupials, *Phascolotherium*, *Amphilestes*, *Amphitherium*, and *Amphitylus*, all belonging to the same family, and *Stereognathus*, of a family by itself, whose position among the Marsupials is by some considered to be doubtful, as in a less degree is that of *Amphitherium*, which has a larger number of teeth than any living member of the order.

No mammals have been found in any of the overlying Jurassic beds until we reach the Purbecks at the top of the series, which differ so markedly in character from those below. In this group, which is largely composed of freshwater deposits, and contains among its numerous fossils a few genera of lake and river shells that still exist, a series of estuarine and shallow marine strata is placed between an upper and lower set of freshwater origin, and near the base of these middle beds a band some five inches thick in Durdlestone Bay has yielded no less than eleven genera of Marsupials, none larger than a rat.

These consist of four species of *Plagiaulax*, one species of *Bolodon*, three species of *Triconodon*, four species of *Amblotherium*, two species of *Achyrodon*, one species of *Kurtodon*, one of *Peramus*, two species of *Stylodon*, one species of *Leptocladus*, two species of *Spalacotherium*, and one of *Peralestes*, making twenty-two species altogether, really a remarkable assemblage for so limited a field.

In the superposed secondary rocks of this country no mammalian fossils have been recorded, or, at least, nothing structural to which a name can be given, but in North America the upper beds of the cretaceous series have yielded a number of small mammals closely allied to the forms from the Rhætics and Purbecks above mentioned, thus indicating that the chain of mammalian life was unbroken, although the links were preserved in a different area. That the mammals of the land should be found in a sea deposit like the chalk is hardly to be expected, but it is not improbable that we may in time light upon their representatives in the fluviatile and littoral deposits of our cretaceous group, such as the Wealden and Lower Greensand.

With the incoming of the Tertiary period we have a different state of things. In the Lower Eocene, mostly in the London Clay, we have discovered our first carnivore, *Argillotherium toliapicum*, one of the Hyænodontidæ; a *Platychœrops*, which seems to be an *Esthonyx*, or, at least, to resemble that genus very closely, one of the extinct order of Tillodonts, which appear to have been ancestral Rodents; two species of *Hyracotherium*, about as large as a hare and with affinities to the tapirs; two species of *Coryphodon*, which were not unlike bears, with feet like those of the elephant, the genus being well represented in the Eocene of North America; and, in addition to these, as a reminder of the early importance of the marsupials, there is an opossum, *Didelphys colchesteri*, of the same genus as that of the existing North American forms.

In the Middle Eocene we get *Lophiodon*, of the same family as *Hyracotherium*, one of those tapir-like animals, which seem to be the ancestral types from which are descended the modern solid-hoofed ungulates, like the horse and the rhinoceros. At this period the climate of what is now the Isle of Wight and its neighbourhood would seem to have been a warm one, to judge from the vast array of remains of tropical plants, giving a flora of much the same aspect as that of South America and the Malay Peninsula, to which the existing tapirs are confined.

In the Upper Eocene, including the beds of the Hampshire basin, the Headon, Osborne, Bembridge, and Hempstead (or Hamstead) series, generally grouped as Oligocene, in which the conditions of deposit were more favourable, we meet for the first time with a really rich fossil mammalian fauna. In them we have our first and, as yet, only lemur, *Adapis magna*, allied to the lorises but differing from them in having an additional premolar. The insectivores are represented by two species of hedgehog (*Neurogymnurus major* and *N. minor*), and by the closely allied *Microchœrus erinaceus;* and the carnivores by the semi-aquatic *Hyænodon minor* and *Pterodon dasyuroides*, and by a civet, *Viverra hastingsiæ*. The rodents are represented by *Theridomys aquatilis*, and the ungulates by about a dozen genera, including the small and slender Dichodons (*Dichodon cuspidatus* and *D. cervinus*); two species of *Anoplotherium* (*A. commune* and *A. secundarium*), a genus exclusively European, distinguished by having neither horns nor claws, and having three toes and a long tail; two of *Xiphodon*, another long-tailed genus in which the toes were only two in number; one species of *Dacrytherium* (*D. ovinum*), differing from the rest of the family in having a lachrymal fossa; one species of *Diplopus*, known only by its legs and vertebræ; three species of *Hyopotamus*, which, like the next, and almost identical genus, had four toes on each foot, instead of two as in *Diplopus;* three species of *Anthracotherium;* a species each of *Chœropotamus* (*C. gypsorum*) and *Elotherium* (*E. magnum*), still more pig-like in their affinities; five species of *Palæotherium* (*P. magnum*, *P. medium*, *P. crassum*, *P. annectens*, and *P. minus*), a three-toed genus with a much longer neck than is given in the usual restorations; and, to end this list, an *Anchilophus desmaresti*, belonging to the same family. Add to these the first rorqual, *Balænoptera juddi*, from the Brockenhurst beds, which is, however, not the first British whale, that honour being at present held by *Zeuglodon wanklyni*, of the lower-lying Barton Clay, the representative of a different sub-order, in which the teeth, unlike those of living whales, are divisible into incisors, canines, and molars. Our Upper Eocene mammals, it will be noticed, included no marsupials, for by this time these would appear to have moved out of the area never again to return to it.

The Older Pliocene of Europe contains a large assemblage of mammals of species mostly extinct, but many of them conveniently filling up the gaps between existing genera. But in this country where the formation is so poorly represented we have had none of the apes, cats, civets, foxes, bears, oxen, deer, antelopes, rhinoceroses, hippopotamuses, horses, beavers, mice, porcupines, hares, etc., the only mammalian remains being yielded by the shelly sands, known as the Coralline Crag, and confined to two humpback whales of the same genus as the living species, these being *Megaptera affinis* and *M. minuta*, which was not so very minute, as it was as large as the Lesser Rorqual.

Of the Newer Pliocene, made up with us of the other Crags with the Forest-Bed on the top, there is another story to tell. The Red Crag, at the base, is one of the richest hunting grounds known to the geologist. From it have come *Felis pardoides*, an early form of leopard, the extinct *Hyæna antiqua*, and *Hyæna striata* the living striped hyæna of India and North Africa, *Canis primigenius*, an early form of the wolf, and, doubtfully, *Vulpes vulgaris*, the existing fox, who must be mentioned, although it is not unlikely that the specimen got into its place by burrowing. Add to these the bear-like *Hyænarctos* and *Ursus arvernensis*, the giant panda, *Ælurus anglicus*, of a genus now known only in the Himalaya, and *Trichechus huxleyi*, an extinct species of walrus. The rodents are represented by a large beaver, *Castor veterior*, and the beaver-like form, *Trogontherium minus*: the ungulates by the two-forked muntjac, *Cervulus dicranoceros*; one of the Anoplotheres, *Xiphodon platyceps*; two swine, the large *Sus antiquus*, and the small *S. palæochærus*; a tapir (*Tapirus priscus*); one of the three-toed horses (*Hipparion gracile*); two rhinoceroses (*Rhinoceros incisivus* and *R. schleiermacheri*); and no less than four elephants (*Mastodon arvernensis*, *M. borsoni*, *M. longirostris*, and *Elephas meridionalis*). The sirenians, otherwise the mermaids, have a representative in *Halitherium canhami*, their first and only appearance in the British fauna; and, as if to leave no doubt as to the conditions under which the Crag was formed, come quite a crowd of whales, probably enclosed within the shallow sea when in pursuit of food, unless, when dead, they were drifted in by some powerful current. Among them are four right whales (*Balæna affinis*, *B. balænopsis*, *B. insignis*, and *B. primigenia*), two humpbacks (*Megaptera affinis*, as in the Coralline Crag, and *M. similis*), four rorquals (*Balænoptera borealina*, *B. definita*, *B. emarginata*, and *B. garopi*), four species of the extinct genus *Cetotherium* (*C. brialmonti*, *C. dubium*, *C. brevifrons*, *C. hupschi*), and the small *Herpetocetus scaldiensis*, whose affinity with the toothed whales is indicated by the long talon of the mandibular condyle. Reckoning up these species, it will be found that we have no less than fifteen whalebone whales, and to these we must add some twenty-three toothed whales, making thirty-eight in all. Verily, whales must have thriven in the days of the Newer Pliocene! Here are *Kogia breviceps*, the small sperm whale still existent; *Physeterula dubusi*, another small edition of the sperm whale; *Eucetus amblyodon*, closely allied, of which there are a large number of specimens; *Balænodon physaloides*, of which there is only one; two species of *Physodon* (*P. fusiformis* and *P. grandis*), both small: three of *Hoplocetus* (*H. borgerhoutensis, H. crassidens* and *H. curvidens*), with enamel caps to the teeth, as in *Physodon;* one species of *Hyperoodon*, no other than the common bottlenose of the North Atlantic (*H. rostratus*); three species of *Choneziphius* (*C. packardi, C. planus*, and *C. planirostris*), the genus with the fistular hole through the short, thick beak, but which in other details of the skull comes intermediate between *Hyperoodon* and *Mesoplodon*, of which no less than seven species have been recorded (*M. floweri, M. longirostris, M. tenuirostris, M. gibbus, M. angustus, M. angulatus,* and *M. compressus*), all of them of much the same character as the living Sowerby's whale (*M. bidens*). In addition to these are *Squalodon antwerpiensis*, one of the extinct shark-toothed dolphins; *Orca citoniensis*, a killer, represented to-day by the larger *O. gladiator;* and *Globicephalus uncidens*, an extinct species of the same genus as the living pilot whale (*G. melas*).

In the Norwich Crag we find the common otter (*Lutra vulgaris*), an extinct beaver (*Trogontherium cuvieri*), a vole (*Microtus intermedius*), a gazelle (*Gazelle anglica*), three deer (*Cervus falconeri, C. verticornis*, and *C. carnutorum*), the first allied to the fallow deer, the second with short, heavy antlers placed obliquely on the frontals, the brow-tine curving downwards and cylindrical, and having two oval tines above it. Besides these there are Steno's horse (*Equus stenonis*) and two elephants (*Elephas antiquus* and *Mastodon arvernensis.*)

Our uppermost deposit of Pliocene age is the Forest-Bed of Norfolk and Suffolk, in which the fauna still more resembles in character that of the present day. Associated with the remains of plants, most of which are now living in the neighbourhood, are many existing molluscs, fishes, reptiles, and mammals, the mammals being of exceptional interest. Here we meet with the mole, *Talpa europæa*, and the Russian desman, *Myogale moschata*, both as we now have them, and the two British land shrews, *Sorex vulgaris* and *S. minutus*. The carnivores are represented by *Machærodus cultridens*, one of the sabre-toothed tigers with long narrow canines, the cave bear, *Ursus spelæus*, as large as the Polar species, Huxley's walrus (*Rosmarus huxleyi*) and the existing pine marten, otter, and bearded seal, besides the wolverene or glutton, *Gulo luscus*, now confined to the northerly regions of the northern hemisphere.

The rodents include the common squirrel and beaver, and the large beaver-like *Trogontherium cuvieri*, also found in the Norwich Crag, and the wood mouse, *Mus sylvaticus*, the continental field vole, *Microtus arvalis*, the Siberian vole, *M. gregalis*, and the bank vole, *M. glareolus*. The musk-ox of Arctic America (*Ovibos moschata*) and *Caprovis savini*, an intermediate form between the sheep and the goat, represent the Bovidæ, and there are some ten species of deer, these being *Alces latifrons*, the broad-fronted moose in which the antlers were less palmated than in the existing species, the present roe deer and red deer, *Cervus polignacus* allied to the fallow deer, *C. tetraceros* whose antlers are not unlike those of the Virginian deer, *C. suttonensis* with the deep groove in the antler beam, and the five species named after Dawkins, Fitch, Gunn, Savin, and

Sedgwick respectively, the last being the most noticeable on account of the many forkings of its magnificent antlers, which have more points than those of any other member of the family. Among the other land mammals were the wild boar, *Sus scrofa*—its first appearance—an extinct *Rhinoceros* (*R. etruscus*), the wild horse (*Equus caballus*)—its first appearance—Steno's horse (*E. stenonis*), and three elephants (*Elephas antiquus, E. meridionalis*, and *E. primigenius*, this being the first appearance of the mammoth). The Biscay or Southern Right whale (*Balæna australis*) also appears for the first time, as do the sperm whale, the narwhal, the porpoise, and the dolphin.

In the Pleistocene age, as revealed by the glacial groups of which its deposits are mainly composed, the life of this area was not so very much unlike what it was when the historic period began. The advance and retirement of the glaciers have left their traces not only on the rock structure, but on the fauna, which clearly indicates the influence of the alternations of cold and warmth. As in America, where the ice moved southwards into New England, and drove the Arctic animals down for a time, so was it in Europe, where the reindeer was driven into Switzerland, the wolverene into the Auvergne, and the musk-ox into the Pyrenees; and the British area, from its position, experienced these alternations to the full, the result being the wide range, climatically, of our Pleistocene mammals. Here we have our first and only monkey (*Macacus pliocenus*), the lion (*Felis leo*), the spotted hyæna (*Hyæna crocuta*), now of South Africa, the brown bear (*Ursus arctus*), which survived in this country into the historic period), the grizzly bear (*U. horribilis*), now confined to North America, and the cave-bear (*U. spelæus*) we met with in the Forest Bed. Here are the polecat, the stoat, and the badger—their first appearances—and the common seal, the ringed seal, and the harp seal—also their first appearances. Among the rodents are a suslik (*Spermophilus altaicus*) from the Arctic Freshwater Bed at the bottom of the series, and another species (*Sp. erythrogenoides*) from a higher horizon. The beaver was there, as also were the common domestic mouse, which has been everywhere since, the field vole (*Microtus agrestis*), and the water vole, otherwise the water rat (*M. amphibius*). Our wild ox (*Bos taurus*) was there, but of larger proportions, so was the equally gigantic European bison (*B. bonasus*), so were the musk-ox and, unexpectedly, the saiga antelope of the Steppes (*Saiga tartarica*). The moose and reindeer put in their first appearances, the latter to remain until after the Norman Conquest, the red deer, as magnificently developed as the oxen, was there, as were also Brown's fallow-deer (*Cervus browni*), the great Irish elk (*C. giganteus*), and the roebuck. Among the other animals were the wild boar and the surviving hippopotamus, the woolly rhinoceros (*Rhinoceros antiquitatis*), with two other species (*R. leptorhinus* and *R. megarhinus*), also with two horns; the wild horse (*Equus caballus*), which has not been found in the country since; the three elephants, as in the Forest Bed, the gigantic southern species (*Elephas meridionalis*), fifteen feet high, the straight-tusked species (*E. antiquus*), allied to the present African elephant, and the mammoth (*E. primigenius*), more of the Indian type, with the hairy coat suited to a colder climate. And among the whales, which included the sperm whale, we have the first appearances of the living humpback (*Megaptera boops*), common rorqual and northern rorqual, pilot whale, and bottlenose dolphin (*Tursiops tursio*).

In the fauna of the caves we have the transition between that of the present and that of the Pleistocene. In the main we may look upon this fauna as prehistoric in the geological sense, though many of the deposits must have occurred in Pleistocene times, many within the historic period, and some evidently must have been continuous up to quite recent years. For our purpose the point is without importance; it is enough for us to know what mammals existed in our country between the early days after its final separation from the continent and the beginning of the records which developed into the " British List " that forms the basis of this book.

In the caves then we find the greater horseshoe bat and the noctule, which may or may not have been early arrivals or survivals, but it is their first appearance, and they are the only bats that the cavern floors have yielded. The hedgehog was a cave-dweller—it is his first appearance—so was the common shrew, harmless creatures both. But another cave-dweller was *Machærodus latidens*, a sabre-toothed tiger, which had both edges of its upper canines with serrations like those of a saw—a by no means harmless companion—and with him were *Felis brevirostris* and the Kaffir cat (*F. caffra*), now living in Asia and Africa, which is the probable ancestor of most of our domestic cats, and besides these there were the existing wild cat (*F. catus*) and the lion, lynx, and leopard, the spotted hyæna, the wolf—to stay with us until 1743—the common fox, the Arctic fox, and a hunting-dog (*Lycaon anglicus*) almost identical with that now in South Africa. There were three bears (the brown bear, grizzly, and cave-bear), the pine-marten, polecat, stoat, weasel, and wolverene, and the badger and the otter. The cave rodents include the beaver, the common mouse, the brown rat, the field vole, the northern vole, continental field vole, water vole, and bank vole, one of the hamsters (*Cricetus songarus*), the Norwegian lemming (*Myodes lemmus*), and the banded lemming (*Cuniculus torquatus*), now of the Arctic regions, one of the pikas (*Lagomys pusillus*), now existing in Northern Europe and Asia, the common hare, the mountain hare, and the rabbit. The wild ox was there, as were the European bison, the sheep, and the goat, the moose, reindeer, red deer, and Irish elk; and also there were the wild boar and hippopotamus, the woolly, leptorhine, and megarhine rhinoceroses, the straight-tusked elephant and the mammoth. Many of them evidently had the run of the cave as now, some of them must have used the cave as a den, some must have been brought in whole or in fragments as prey, and some may have crept in to die. Any way, there is no doubt that these animals lived in our country, and that it is in these caves we meet with the last traces of our lions, lynxes, leopards, hyænas, hippopotamuses, rhinoceroses, and elephants, in whose existence some people find it so difficult to believe.

They are certainly in a strict sense our country's animals, and as such ought to figure in a systematic list. Such a list we have not yet seen, but that is no reason why we should not have one here; and as it will be more useful with the living species included.

we will fill them in as they come, in the same order as before, with their distinguishing numbers, and call it—

BRITISH MAMMALS PAST AND PRESENT.

PRIMATES.

ANTHROPOIDEA.

CERCOPITHECIDÆ.

Macacus pliocenus (Pleistocene).

LEMUROIDEA.

LEMURIDÆ.

Adapis magna (Upper Eocene).

CHIROPTERA.

RHINOLOPHIDÆ.

1. Rhinolophus ferrum-equinum (Caves and Existent), Greater Horse-shoe Bat.
2. Rhinolophus hipposiderus (Existent), Lesser Horse-shoe Bat.

VESPERTILIONIDÆ.

3. Plecotus auritus (Existent), Long-eared bat.
4. Synotus barbastellus (Existent), Barbastelle.
5. Vesperugo serotinus (Existent), Serotine.
6. Vesperugo discolor (Existent), Parti-coloured Bat.
7. Vesperugo noctula (Caves and Existent), Noctule.
8. Vesperugo leisleri (Existent), Hairy-armed Bat.
9. Vesperugo pipistrellus (Existent), Pipistrelle.
10. Vespertilio dasycneme (Existent), Rough-legged Bat.
11. Vespertilio daubentoni (Existent), Daubenton's Bat.
12. Vespertilio nattereri (Pleistocene and Existent), Reddish-grey Bat.
13. Vespertilio bechsteini (Existent), Bechstein's Bat.
14. Vespertilio murinus (Existent), Mouse-coloured Bat
15. Vespertilio mystacinus (Existent), Whiskered Bat,

INSECTIVORA.

ERINACEIDÆ.

16. Erinaceus europæus, (Caves and Existent), Hedgehog.
Neurogymnurus major (Upper Eocene).
Neurogymnurus minor (Upper Eocene).

MICROCHŒRIDÆ.

Microchœrus erinaceus (Upper Eocene).

TALPIDÆ.

17. Talpa europæa (Forest Bed and Existent), Mole.
Myogale moschata (Forest Bed and Existent in South-east Russia), Russian Desman.

SORICIDÆ.

18. Sorex vulgaris (Forest Bed, Pleistocene, Caves, and Existent), Common Shrew.
19. Sorex minutus (Forest Bed, Pleistocene, and Existent), Lesser Shrew.
20. Crossopus fodiens (Existent), Water Shrew.

CARNIVORA.

FELIDÆ.

Machærodus cultridens (Forest Bed).
Machærodus latidens (Caves).
Felis brevirostris (Caves).
Felis caffra (Caves and Existent in Africa and Asia), Kaffir Cat.

21. Felis catus (Caves and Existent), Wild Cat.
Felis leo (Pleistocene, Caves, and Existent in Africa and Asia), Lion.
Felis lynx (Caves and Existent in Northern Europe and Asia), Lynx.
Felis pardus (Caves and Existent in Asia and Africa), Leopard.
Felis pardoides (Red Crag).

HYÆNIDÆ

Hyæna antiqua (Red Crag).
Hyæna crocuta (Pleistocene, Caves, and Existent in South Africa), Spotted Hyæna.

Hyæna striata (Red Crag and Existent in North Africa and India), Striped Hyæna.

HYÆNODONTIDÆ.

Hyænodon minor (Upper Eocene).
Pterodon dasyuroides (Upper Eocene).
Argillotherium toliapicum (Lower Eocene).

VIVERRIDÆ.

Viverra hastingsiæ (Upper Eocene).

CANIDÆ.

Canis lupus (Caves and Existent in Northern Hemisphere. Extinct in the British area since 1743), Wolf.
Canis primigenius (Red Crag).

22. Vulpes vulgaris (Red Crag, Pleistocene, Caves, and Existent), Fox.
Vulpes lagopus (Pleistocene, Caves, and Existent in Northern Hemisphere), Arctic Fox.
Lycaon anglicus (Caves).

URSIDÆ.

Hyænarctos (Red Crag).
Ursus arctos (Pleistocene, Caves, and Existent in Europe and Asia. Extinct in British area since 900), Brown Bear.
Ursus arvernensis (Red Crag).
Ursus horribilis (Pleistocene, Caves, and Existent in North America), Grizzly Bear.
Ursus spelæus (Forest Bed, Pleistocene, and Caves), Cave Bear.

PROCYONIDÆ.

Ælurus anglicus (Red Crag).

MUSTELIDÆ.

23. Mustela martes (Forest Bed, Caves, and Existent), Pine Marten.
Putorius robustus (Pleistocene).

24. Putorius fœtidus (Pleistocene, Caves, and Existent), Polecat.

25. Putorius erminea (Pleistocene, Caves, and Existent), Stoat.

26. Putorius hibernicus (Existent), Irish Stoat.

27. Putorius vulgaris (Pleistocene, Caves, and Existent), Weasel.
    Gulo luscus (Forest Bed, Caves, and Existent in Northern Hemisphere), Wolverene.

28. Meles taxus (Pleistocene, Caves, and Existent), Badger.

29. Lutra vulgaris (Norwich Crag, Forest Bed, Pleistocene, Caves, and Existent), Otter.

TRICHECIDÆ.

Trichecus rosmarus (Prehistoric and Existent in Arctic Ocean. Not recorded in British area since 1841), Walrus.
Trichecus huxleyi (Red Crag and Forest Bed).

PHOCIDÆ.

30. Phoca vitulina (Pleistocene and Existent), Common Seal.

31. Phoca hispida (Pleistocene and Existent), Ringed Seal.

32. Phoca grœnlandica (Pleistocene and Existent), Harp Seal.
    Phoca barbata (Forest Bed and Existent in North Atlantic), Bearded Seal.

33. Halichœrus grypus (Existent), Grey Seal.

34. Cystophora cristata (Existent), Hooded Seal.

TILLODONTIA.

PLATYCHŒROPIDÆ.

Platychœrops richardsoni (Lower Eocene).

RODENTIA.

SCIURIDÆ.

35. Sciurus vulgaris (Forest Bed and Existent), Squirrel.
    Spermophilus altaicus (Arctic Freshwater Bed).

Spermophilus erythrogenoides (Pleistocene and Caves).

CASTORIDÆ.

Castor fiber (Forest Bed, Pleistocene, Caves, and Existent in northern hemisphere. Extinct in British area since 1188, but re-introduced under preservation), Beaver.
Castor veterior (Red Crag).
Trogontherium cuvieri (Norwich Crag and Forest Bed).
Trogontherium minus (Red Crag).

MYOXIDÆ.

36. Muscardinus avellanarius (Existent), Dormouse.

MURIDÆ.

37. Mus minutus (Existent), Harvest Mouse.
Mus lewisi (Pleistocene).

38. Mus sylvaticus (Forest Bed and Existent), Wood Mouse.

39. Mus sylvaticus wintoni (Existent), Yellow-necked Mouse.

40. Mus musculus (Pleistocene, Caves, and Existent), Common Mouse.

41. Mus rattus (Existent), Black Rat.

42. Mus decumanus (Caves and Existent), Brown Rat.

43. Microtus agrestis (Pleistocene, Caves, and Existent), Field Vole.

44. Microtus amphibius (Pleistocene, Caves, and Existent), Water Vole.
Microtus arvalis (Forest Bed, Caves, and Existent in Europe), Continental Field Vole.

45. Microtus glareolus (Forest Bed, Caves, and Existent), Bank Vole.
Microtus gregalis (Forest Bed, Caves, and Existent in Northern Asia), Siberian Vole.
Microtus intermedius (Norwich Crag and Forest Bed).
Microtus nivalis (Prehistoric, and Existent in Alps and Pyrenees), Alpine Vole.
Microtus ratticeps (Pleistocene, Caves, and Existent in Northern Europe), Northern Vole.
Cricetus songarus (Caves).

Myodes lemmus (Pleistocene, Caves, and Existent in Scandinavia), Norwegian Lemming.

Cuniculus torquatus (Pleistocene, Caves, and Existent in the Arctic Regions), Banded Lemming.

SPALACIDÆ.

Spalacodon (Upper Eocene).

THERIDOMYIDÆ.

Theridomys aquatilis (Upper Eocene).

LAGOMYIDÆ.

Lagomys pusillus (Pleistocene, Caves, and Existent in Northern Asia and Europe), Pika.

LEPORIDÆ.

46. Lepus europæus (Pleistocene, Caves, and Existent), Common Hare.

47. Lepus timidus (Pleistocene, Caves, and Existent), Mountain Hare.

48. Lepus cuniculus (Caves and Existent), Rabbit.
Lepus diluvianus (Caves).

UNGULATA.

BOVIDÆ.

49. Bos taurus (Pleistocene, Caves, and Existent), Wild Ox.

Bos bonasus (Pleistocene, Caves, and Existent in Eastern Europe), European Bison.

Ovibos moschatus (Forest Bed, Pleistocene, and Existent in Arctic America), Musk Ox.

Ovis aries (Caves, and Existent in Northern Hemisphere), Wild Sheep.

Caprovis savini (Forest Bed).

Capra hircus (Caves, and Existent in Europe and Asia), Wild Goat.

Gazella anglica (Norwich Crag).

Saiga tartarica (Pleistocene, and Existent in Eastern Europe and Western Asia), Saiga Antelope.

CERVIDÆ.

Alces latifrons (Forest Bed).

Alces machlis (Pleistocene, and Existent in Northern hemisphere), Moose.

Rangifer tarandus (Pleistocene, Caves, and Existent in Northern Hemisphere. Extinct in·British area since 1100). Reindeer.

50. Cervus elaphus (Forest Bed, Pleistocene, Caves, and Existent), Red Deer.

51. Cervus dama (Existent), Fallow Deer.
Cervus browni (Pleistocene), Brown's Fallow Deer.
Cervus carnutorum (Norwich Crag).
Cervus dawkinsi (Forest Bed), Dawkins's Deer.
Cervus falconeri (Norwich Crag), Falconer's Deer.
Cervus fitchi (Forest Bed), Fitch's Deer.
Cervus giganteus (Pleistocene, Caves, and Bogs), Irish Elk.
Cervus gunni (Forest Bed), Gunn's Deer.
Cervus polignacus (Forest Bed).
Cervus savini (Forest Bed), Savin's Deer.
Cervus sedgwicki (Forest Bed), Sedgwick's Deer.
Cervus suttonensis (Red Crag).
Cervus tetraceros (Forest Bed).
Cervus verticornis (Norwich Crag).

52. Capreolus caprea (Forest Bed, Pleistocene, Caves, and Existent), Roe Deer.
Cervulus dicranoceros (Forest Crag), Two-forked Muntjac.

DICHODONTIDÆ.

Dichodon cervinus (Upper Eocene).
Dichodon cuspidatus (Upper Eocene).

CÆNOTHERIIDÆ.

Acotherulum saturninum (Upper Eocene).

ANOPLOTHERIIDÆ.

Anoplotherium commune (Upper Eocene).
Anoplotherium secundarium (Upper Eocene).
Xiphodon gracilis (Upper Eocene).
Xiphodon platyceps (Red Crag).
Dacrytherium ovinum (Upper Eocene).

ANTHRACOTHERIIDÆ.

>Diplopus aymardi (Upper Eocene).
>Hyopotamus bovinus (Upper Eocene).
>Hyopotamus porcinus (Upper Eocene).
>Hyopotamus velaunus (Upper Eocene).
>Anthracotherium alsaticum (Upper Eocene).
>Anthracotherium gresslyi (Upper Eocene).
>Anthracotherium minus (Upper Eocene).

CHŒROPOTAMIDÆ.

>Chœropotamus gypsorum (Upper Eocene).
>Elotherium magnum (Upper Eocene).

SUIDÆ.

>Sus antiquus (Red Crag).
>Sus palæochœrus (Red Crag).
>Sus scrofa (Forest Bed, Pleistocene, Caves, and Existent in Europe and North Africa. Extinct in British area since 1593), Wild Boar.

HIPPOPOTAMIDÆ.

>Hippopotamus amphibius (Pleistocene, Caves, and Existent in Africa), Hippopotamus.

TAPIRIDÆ.

>Tapirus priscus (Red Crag).

LOPHIODONTIDÆ.

>Lophiodon minimus (Middle Eocene).
>Hyracotherium leporinum (Lower Eocene).
>Hyracotherium cuniculus (Lower Eocene).

PALÆOTHERIIDÆ.

>Palæotherium annectens (Upper Eocene).
>Palæotherium crassum (Upper Eocene).
>Palæotherium magnum (Upper Eocene).
>Palæotherium medium (Upper Eocene).
>Palæotherium minus (Upper Eocene).
>Anchilophus desmaresti (Upper Eocene).

EQUIDÆ.

Hipparion gracile (Red Crag).

Equus caballus (Forest Bed, Pleistocene, Caves, and Existent in Central Asia), Wild Horse.

Equus stenonis (Norwich Crag and Forest Bed), Steno's Horse.

RHINOCEROTIDÆ.

Rhinoceros antiquitatis (Pleistocene and Caves), Woolly Rhinoceros.

Rhinoceros etruscus (Forest Bed).

Rhinoceros incisivus (Red Crag).

Rhinoceros leptorhinus (Pleistocene and Caves).

Rhinoceros megarhinus (Pleistocene and Caves).

Rhinoceros schleiermacheri (Red Crag).

CORYPHODONTIDÆ.

Coryphodon croydonensis (Lower Eocene).

Coryphodon eocænus (Lower Eocene).

ELEPHANTIDÆ.

Mastodon arvernensis (Red Crag and Norwich Crag)

Mastodon borsoni (Red Crag).

Mastodon longirostris (Red Crag).

Elephas antiquus (Norwich Crag, Forest Bed, Pleistocene, and Caves), Straight-tusked Elephant.

Elephas meridionalis (Red Crag, Forest Bed, and Pleistocene), Southern Elephant.

Elephas primigenius (Forest Bed, Pleistocene, and Caves), Mammoth.

SIRENIA.

HALITHERIIDÆ.

Halitherium canhami (Red Crag).

CETACEA.

BALÆNIDÆ.

Balæna affinis (Red Crag).

53. Balæna australis (Forest Bed and Existent), Biscay Whale.

Balæna balænopsis (Red Crag).

Balæna insignis (Red Crag).

Balæna mysticetus (Prehistoric and Existent in Arctic Ocean), Greenland Whale.

Balæna primigenia (Red Crag).

Palæocetus sedgwicki (Boulder Clay).

Megaptera affinis (Coralline Crag and Red Crag).

Megaptera minuta (Coralline Crag).

Megaptera similis (Red Crag).

54. Megaptera boops (Pleistocene and Existent), Humpback Whale.

Balænoptera borealina (Red Crag).

55. Balænoptera sibbaldii (Existent), Sibbald's Rorqual.

56. Balænoptera musculus (Pleistocene and Existent), Common Rorqual.

57. Balænoptera borealis (Pleistocene and Existent), Northern Rorqual.

58. Balænoptera rostrata (Existent), Lesser Rorqual.

Balænoptera definita (Red Crag).

Balænoptera emarginata (Red Crag).

Balænoptera garopi (Red Crag).

Balænoptera juddi (Middle Eocene).

Eschrichtius robustus (Pleistocene).

Cetotherium brevifrons (Red Crag).

Cetotherium brialmonti (Red Crag).

Cetotherium dubium (Red Crag).

Cetotherium hupschi (Red Crag).

Herpetocetus scaldiensis (Red Crag).

ZEUGLODONTIDÆ.

Zeuglodon wanklyni (Upper Eocene).

PHYSETERIDÆ.

59. Physeter macrocephalus (Forest Bed, Pleistocene, and Existent), Sperm Whale.

Kogia breviceps (Red Crag and Existent in Atlantic and Pacific), Lesser Sperm Whale.

Physeterula dubusi (Red Crag).

Eucetus amblyodon (Red Crag).

Balænodon physaloides (Red Crag).

Physodon fusiformis (Red Crag).

Physodon grandis (Red Crag).

Hoplocetus borgerhoutensis (Red Crag).

Hoplocetus crassidens (Red Crag).

Hoplocetus curvidens (Red Crag).

60. Hyperoodon rostratus (Red Crag and Existent),
    Bottlenose Whale.
    Choneziphius packardi (Red Crag).
    Choneziphius planirostris (Red Crag).
    Choneziphius planus (Red Crag).

61. Mesoplodon bidens (Existent), Sowerby's Whale.
    Mesoplodon floweri (Red Crag).
    Mesoplodon longirostris (Red Crag).
    Mesoplodon tenuirostris (Red Crag).
    Mesoplodon gibbus (Red Crag).
    Mesoplodon angustus (Red Crag).
    Mesoplodon angulatus (Red Crag).
    Mesoplodon compressus (Red Crag).

62. Ziphius cavirostris (Existent), Cuvier's Whale.

SQUALODONTIDÆ.

Squalodon antwerpiensis (Red Crag).

DELPHINIDÆ.

63. Monodon monoceros (Forest Bed and Existent),
    Narwhal.

64. Delphinapterus leucas (Existent), White Whale.

65. Phocæna communis (Forest Bed and Existent),
    Porpoise.

66. Orca gladiator (Existent), Killer.
    Orca citoniensis (Red Crag).
    Pseudorca crassidens (Prehistoric).

67. Globicephalus melas (Pleistocene and Existent),
    Pilot Whale.
    Globicephalus uncidens (Red Crag).

68. Grampus griseus (Existent), Risso's Grampus.

69. Lagenorhynchus albirostris (Existent), White-beaked
    Dolphin.

70. Lagenorhynchus acutus (Existent), White-sided
    Dolphin.

71. Delphinus delphis (Forest Bed and Existent),
    Common Dolphin.

72. Tursiops tursio (Pleistocene and Existent), Bottle-
    nose Dolphin.

MARSUPIALIA.

PLAGIAULACIDÆ.

Plagiaulax becklesi (Middle Purbeck).
Plagiaulax falconeri (Middle Purbeck).
Plagiaulax medius (Middle Purbeck).
Plagiaulax minor (Middle Purbeck).

BOLODONTIDÆ.

Bolodon crassidens (Middle Purbeck).
Microlestes moorei (Rhætic).
Microlestes rhæticus (Rhætic).

TRICONODONTIDÆ.

Triconodon ferox (Middle Purbeck).
Triconodon mordax (Middle Purbeck).
Triconodon major (Middle Purbeck).

AMPHITHERIIDÆ.

Phascolotherium bucklandi (Stonesfield Slate).
Amphilestes broderipi (Stonesfield Slate).
Ampthitherium prevosti (Stonesfield Slate).
Amblotherium dubius (Middle Purbeck).
Amblotherium mustelula (Middle Purbeck).
Amblotherium soricinum (Middle Purbeck).
Amblotherium talpoides (Middle Purbeck).
Achyrodon nanus (Middle Purbeck(.
Achyrodon pusillus (Middle Purbeck).
Amphitylus oweni (Stonesfield Slate).
Kurtodon pusillus (Middle Purbeck).
Peramus tenuirostris (Middle Purbeck).

DIDELPHYIDÆ.

Didelphys colchesteri (Lower Eocene).

STYLODONTIDÆ.

> Stylodon pusillus (Middle Purbeck).
> Stylodon robustus (Middle Purbeck).
> Leptocladus dubius (Middle Purbeck).

SPALACOTHERIIDÆ.

> Spalacotherium tricuspidens (Middle Purbeck).
> Spalacotherium minus (Middle Purbeck).
> Peralestes longirostris (Middle Purbeck).

STEREOGNATHIDÆ.

> Stereognathus ooliticus (Stonesfield Slate).

CHAPTER VI.

IDENTIFICATION.

———◆———

SO far as this country is now concerned, the differences between the orders represented are so marked that there is hardly any difficulty in at once assigning a mammal to its proper group. If it has no hind legs it must be a cetacean; if it has wings it must be a bat; if it has hoofs it must be an ungulate. Practically doubt can only arise in the event of its being a rodent, a carnivore, or an insectivore; and as a carnivore it can at once be distinguished by its prominent canines, as a rodent by its large incisors and the gap where the canines ought to be. Among the insectivores, the hedge-hog and mole are almost as well known as the cat and the dog, and it is in the case of the shrews alone, as evidenced by the popular name of shrew-mice, that mistake is likely. In short, if we know our shrews, the path of identification is easy.

The main points in which a shrew differs from a mouse are these. The shrew has a much longer muzzle than the mouse; in the shrew the tail is hairy, in the mouse it is scaly; in the shrew it is squarish and straight for some distance, in the mouse it is round and tapers from the root to the tip; in the shrew the ears are small and lie flat against the head, in the mouse they are large and prominent. But the great differences are in the teeth. In the shrew the teeth are very small and require a magnifying glass to distinguish them, in the mouse they are fairly large; in the shrew there are eighteen to twenty in the upper jaw and twelve in the lower, in the mouse there are eight in each of the jaws. Thus the shrew has thirty or thirty-two teeth and the mouse only sixteen; those of the shrew are continuous, those of the mouse have a large gap in the row and this is filled by the hairy skin; the mouse has only two incisors, the shrew has more than two; those of the mouse are flat and chisel edged, those of the shrew are pointed; in the shrew the canines are much the same as the incisors, the mouse has no canines at all; the shrew has three premolars, the mouse has no premolars, ; in fact, the only teeth the mouse has are two incisors and six molars, three a side, top and bottom. Of course there are other differences, but these are enough to show that the shrew is an insectivore and the mouse a rodent, which is all we intended to do.

And now let us take a bat and find out its name. The first things to look for are the leaf-like appendages the nostrils, which, when present, are the most prominent feature of the head. The bat we have chosen is not one of the horseshoes, and consequently has no nose-leaf. Clearly, then, its family is Vespertilionidæ, as is further shown by the presence of the earlet within the ear. Are the ears united at their base? No, and it can be neither the long-eared species nor the Barbastelle. Does the margin of the ear end opposite the inner edge of the earlet, or does it extend to the angle of the mouth? It reaches very nearly to the mouth. The genus is *Vesperugo*. Turning to our preceding chapter we find that the genus is divisible into two groups, those in which the wing membrane rises from the base of the toes, and those in which it rises from the ankle. Our specimen belongs to the first of these groups. It must, therefore, be one of three. Look at the membrane near the spur, if that is narrow the bat is the Serotine; but the membrane is broad, so that it must be one of the other two, as is evident from its size, for it is under two inches in length, though about eight inches across the wings. It is not, however, the parti-coloured bat, as its colour is reddish brown, and not brown and white, and we are therefore safe in assuming that it is the Pipistrelle, an opinion in which we are confirmed when we refer to the brief description of that species in the notes.

An insectivore will give us much less trouble. If it is spiny it is a hedgehog; if it has no ears it is a mole; if it has ears and not a spiny coat it is a shrew; if its feet are fringed with hair, and its tail has a long, hairy fringe below, it is the water shrew; if not, it is one of the two land shrews, *Sorex*, and a reference to that genus in the fifth chapter will show which.

A carnivore will give us a longer run, though we will not choose the fox, but something smaller. It is not a seal, but unmistakably an animal of the land. Count its hind toes. There are five of them. Then it is neither a cat nor a fox, for they have but four. Are its toes webbed? No. Then it is not an otter. Has it a long tail? No. Then it is not a marten. Are its fore claws longer than its hind claws? No. Then it is not a badger, and its genus can only be *Putorius*. But which of the four species? Has it a black tip to its tail? No. Then it is neither of the Stoats. Its tail is tipped with brown, its body is brown on the back and sides and white underneath, and it is about six inches long. In fact, our carnivore is a Weasel.

As an example of the rodents we cannot do better than take a mouse. Is its tail long or short? Long. Is the tail hairy or scaly? Hairy. Then it is the Dormouse, as we shall find by the presence of the one pair of premolars in each jaw. But a Dormouse is not a mouse in all senses; let us take one in which the tail is short and hairy. It must be one of the Voles, as a glance at its teeth will show, for it will have no premolars at all, and its molars will be divided into a series of alternate triangles. It is not over six inches in length, and consequently is not the Water Vole, and it is greyish and not chestnut on the back, so that it must be the Field Vole, as we can assure ourselves by counting the number of its teeth prisms. One more British rodent, this time with a long scaly tail. It can belong to no other genus than *Mus*, and as it is under five inches long, barring the tail, it is not a rat unless it be a young one, and then the length of its proximal foot-pad, as described in our notes, will betray it. In short, it is a mouse; but which of the four? Are its hind feet brown, white, or grey? They are grey, so it is the Common Mouse. Are its ears short and broad? They are long and rounded, again the only alternative is Common Mouse; and a reference to the further points mentioned in the notes confirms the diagnosis.

In dealing with the cetaceans the first thing is to see if there are any teeth. If there are none there will be whalebone, and the animal must be one of the six whalebone whales, readily distinguishable from each other by their fins and flippers. If there are teeth only in the lower jaw it will either be Risso's Grampus or one of the four Physeteridæ, probably the Bottlenose; if there are teeth in both jaws it will be one of the dolphin family. Should the beak be long, the species must, as shown by our table, be one of two; either it is the Bottlenose Dolphin, in which the pairs of teeth total up to twenty-one or less, or else the Common Dolphin, when its pairs of teeth will be forty or more, its jaws will be equal in length, and its palate will be grooved.

Let our last example be a still commoner cetacean belonging to the beakless group. It is not grey in colour, so it is not the Narwhal; it is not white, and so cannot be the White Whale; it is not almost entirely black, and so is not the Black Whale. It is black above and white below, almost half and half in fact, but having no white spot over the eye, no particularly tall dorsal fin, and more than a dozen pairs of teeth; thus it cannot be the Killer, but must be the Porpoise, as its many spatulate teeth sufficiently show.

An outline sketch of a skull is given with every genus, for the skull is almost as often found as the living animal, and so far as the genus is concerned is as easily distinguishable. The six orders are by it recognisable at a glance; there is no mistaking the peculiar dentition of the bats and insectivores, the canines and carnassials of the carnivores, and, when the carnassials are absent, the peculiar dental equipment of the seals. The incisors of the rodents are quite as noticeable, the heads of cattle and deer are as well known as those of horses and sheep, and the cetacean skull has a character of its own that cannot be mistaken. In examining a skull look first at the teeth, as regards their number, character, and arrangement, then observe the peculiarities of the lower jawbone and its junction with the squamosal, close to which will be found the auditory bulla or tympanic, and then examine the frontal, particularly as to the absence or presence of the postorbital, that small shelf-like process over the eye which we have found so useful as a guide.

The most easily recognisable characteristics are mentioned in the notes, which are given mainly for the purpose of confirming the identification. For further details as to structure, habits, and localities, reference must be made to the many works, more or less technical, in which the animal may not appear under the name herein adopted, but under some other in the following fairly complete list of the synonyms of the British mammals in use at various times during the last hundred years.

CHAPTER VII.

THE BRITISH REPTILES.

————◆————

THERE are but nine British reptiles, and with the exception of the three lizards, these all belong to different genera. The seven genera represent six different families belonging to five orders and two of the sub-classes. These sub-classes are Chelonia (turtles and tortoises), and Sauria (lizards and snakes), and of each two orders of the first, Atheca and Thecophora, there is one example, while both the Saurian orders, Lacertilia and Ophidia are represented by two families.

The Chelonians are distinctive enough to be summarily dealt with. The Leathery Turtle (*Sphargis*, 74) has the shell covered with leathery skin without epidermal shields; the Hawksbill (*Chelone*, 73) has the shell covered with horny shields. Needless to say, both these turtles have become British by misadventure.

The snakes and lizards, which are all genuine Britons, with one doubtful exception, require more careful treatment. There are two orders of Sauria :—

1. Lacertilia, in which the right and left halves of the lower jaw are united by a bony suture.

2. Ophidia, in which the bony suture is replaced by an elastic ligament.

This seems but a feeble and ultra-technical way of separating the lizards from the snakes, but it is really the only essential difference. The presence or absence of legs is no guide, as among the ophidians are the pythons, boas, and cylinder snakes, which have external vestiges of hind limbs, and among the lizards are some which have no visible legs, as, for instance, the Slow-worm (*Anguis*) which is the first lizard on the British list, and is thereby distinguishable from the other three, all of which have legs. Our first table is consequently simple.

LACERTILIA—
   1. (Anguidæ)—
      No visible legs. *Anguis*, 75.

   2. (Lacertidæ)—
      Legs well developed. *Lacerta*, 76 to 78,

Of the three snakes, one, the Viper, is the sole representative of a family in which the upper jaw is toothless except for the fangs and their reserves, and in which the hinder upper jawbones can be vertically raised ; and the Viper can be further distinguished from its two compatriots by having its labial shields separated from its eye by scales. In the Ringed Snake and Smooth Snake the upper jaw is fully toothed, the hinder upper jawbones are fixed horizontally, and the labial shields extend right up to the eye without any intervening row of scales. Thus we can finish this sorting out of our reptilian genera with

OPHIDIA—

   1. (Colubridæ)—

      Both jaws fully toothed ; hinder upper maxillaries fixed horizontally ; labial shields extending to eye.
      Scales keeled, *Tropidonotus*, 79.
      Scales smooth, *Coronella*, 80.

   2. (Viperidæ)—

      Upper jaws toothless except for the fangs and their reserves; hinder upper maxillaries capable of vertical erection; labial shields separated from the eye by scales. *Vipera*, 81.

But useful as this may be as a ready means of identification, something more is needed by way of description, and that can best be given in a more formal way. Let us then begin again at the beginning and work our way down from the class to the families. What are reptiles ? Reptiles are cold-blooded vertebrates clothed with scales or scutes instead of hair or feathers. They breathe by lungs throughout life, and their skull articulates with the backbone by a median occipital condyle, and their lower jaw articulates with the skull by a quadrate bone. They are grouped in ten sub-classes, of which only two, Chelonia and Sauria, are represented in the British list of living animals, the Chelonians owing their place therein to a few drifted specimens of only two species.

The characteristics of the Chelonia are briefly as follows. They are oviparous reptiles with a broad, flat, compact body encased within a bony shell of dermal bones, of which the dorsal series is known as the carapace and the ventral as the plastron. The carapace is formed of the neural spines of the vertebræ, of the expanded ribs, and a series of marginal plates round the outer edge; the plastron is formed of the clavicles and a few other elements. The carapace and plastron may or may not be covered with horny plates known as tortoiseshell, in which many nerves terminate. The quadrate is firmly joined to the skull and does not move. There is no sternum. The ribs have their capitular portions only ; there are two sacral vertebræ. The jaws have cutting horny sheaths and no teeth, except in a rudimentary state in the embryo. The sub-class is made up of two orders, Atheca and Thecophora.

In the Thecophora the dorsal vertebræ and ribs are expanded into bony plates forming the carapace, and the parietal bones are prolonged downwards to meet the pterygoids directly or indirectly. There are three sub-orders; in one of these the carapace is very flat, almost round, and covered with leathery skin instead of horny shields, in the other two the carapace (except in one genus) is covered with horny shields. The genus is *Carettochelys*, the sub-order to which it belongs being Pleurodira, which consists entirely of freshwater tortoises. These are recognised by the neck bending laterally and being retracted into the space between the forepart of the carapace and plastron, and by the pelvis being united with the shell. They are not represented in this country.

In the Cryptodira, the third sub-order, the carapace is covered with horny shields. The neck, if retractile, bends in a sigmoid curve in a vertical plane, and the pelvis is not united with the shell. The transverse processes of the cervicals are almost or entirely wanting; the centrum of the last cervical articulates with the centrum of the first dorsal. The pterygoids are narrow in the middle and touch along their inner edges. There are six families, only one of which, the Chelonidæ, has a British representative.

In the Chelonidæ the neck is incompletely retractile and short; the temples are roofed over by the expanded parietals and adjoining bones, the parietals being in contact with the squamosals; the shell is heart-shaped, the limbs are paddle-shaped and widened by the enlarged pisiform bone; in the fore paddle the phalanges of the digits are 2, 3, 3, 2, 2, in the hind-paddle there is one more joint in the fourth digit. This is the family of the Sea-Turtles, and of them we have but one representative, the Hawksbill (Plate xxvii., 73).

In the Atheca the vertebræ and ribs are separate from the carapace, which consists of small polygonal plates covered with leathery skin. In the skull the parietal bones are without descending processes. The neck is not retractile; the limbs are in the shape of paddles and without claws. There is but one family, Sphargidæ, and this consists of a single genus, which in its turn has but one species, the Leathery Turtle (Plate xxvii., 74).

Our two Chelonians appear so seldom on our shores that they may be regarded rather as accidental immigrants than as occasional visitors. With our seven Saurians it is different. They are all undoubtedly native, all, perhaps, but one which may have ceased to be English, but remains British from its breeding as usual in the Channel Islands.

In the Saurians the quadrate bone is more or less movable, and has its lower end projecting; there is no lower temporal arch; the ribs of the back are single-headed, and join on to a facet at the side of the body of the vertebræ instead of to the junction between the vertebræ as in the Chelonians, or to the arches on them as in the Crocodiles and Plesiosaurs; there is no plastron, nor are there any abdominal ribs, properly so-called; and the teeth are not implanted in sockets, but fixed direct to the surface of the bones. This, the dominant division of reptiles, is formed of two, or rather three, orders if the Chameleons be separated from the others; but as these (Rhiptoglossa) are not represented with us, we need say no more about them, and can confine our attention to the two groups of far greater importance, the lizards (Lacertilia) and the snakes (Ophidia).

In the Lacertilia the branches of the lower jaw are firmly connected by a bony suture, so that the mouth is not expansible; the nasal bones enter the border of the nasal apertures, the pterygoid touches the quadrate, the vomers are distinct; the tongue is not retractile into a basal sheath. Most lizards have limbs, all of them have shoulder girdle and hip girdle more or less developed, even when there are no limbs; most of them have movable eyelids and external ear-openings, and have the back and sides covered with overlapping scales. There are nineteen or twenty orders, with only two of which—Anguidæ and Lacertidæ—we have here to deal.

In the Anguidæ the body is rigid and protected by tubuliferous bony plates beneath the scales; the scales are overlapping; the head has symmetrical shields on the upper surface, with a large occipital shield at the back. The tongue is rather long, the hinder part bifid and thick and covered with villose papillæ, the fore part emarginate and thin and covered with scaly papillæ, and extrusible and retractile into a fold in the villose portion. The teeth are solid, and, after the first set, grow between the bases of their predecessors. The premaxillary is single, the nasals distinct, the parietals single. The supratemporal fossa has a bony roof. The clavicle is slender, the shoulder girdle and hip girdle being always present although there may be no limbs. The tail is long, brittle, and reproducible. There are seven genera, some of which are viviparous; only one, *Anguis*, is British (Plate xxviii., 75).

In the Lacertidæ the body is not rigid and there are no bony plates beneath the scales. The dorsal scales are arranged side by side or overlap, and are keeled or otherwise, large or small, but usually smaller than the ventrals, which are broader than long and generally placed in well-marked rows. The shields of the head are symmetrical, mingled with small scales, and attached to the underlying bones. The tongue is flat, long, bifid at both ends, and covered with scaly papillæ. The teeth are hollow at their bases, and have mostly two or three cusps. The premaxillary is single, the nasals distinct, the parietal single. The supratemporal fossa has a bony roof, but is practically wanting, owing to the enlargement of the post-frontal. The clavicle is dilated, the inter-clavicle cruciform. The limbs are well developed, with five digits on each, all with sharp claws. The back of the thigh is poriferous. The tail is long, pointed, and brittle. The ears are exposed, so are the eyes, with their round pupils and distinct lids. There are twenty genera, of which only one, *Lacerta*, is British (Plate xxviii., 76 to 78).

In the Ophidia the mouth is expansible owing to the branches of the lower jaw being connected, not by a bony suture, but by an elastic ligament. The nasal bones form a border round the nasal apertures. The pterygoid, when present, is long; it is generally attached to the quadrate, and in many cases touches the mandibles. The vomer is distinct. The tongue is smooth, flat, and bifid, and retractile into a sheath. The limbs and girdles, when present, are vestigial. There are no external ears. The eyes are immovable, and there are no movable eyelids, the lid being a transparent scale of the horny epidermis. The head scales are large plates, the ventral scales are transverse shields. There are nine orders, only two of which, Colubridæ and Viperidæ, are represented in our list.

In the Colubridæ both jaws are toothed ; the mandible has no coronoid ; the maxillary is horizontal, and does not rise at a right angle to the transpalatine ; the quadrate is carried by the supratemporal, which is loosely attached to the top of the skull. The facial bones are movable. To this order belong nine-tenths of the living snakes. It is divided into three groups, one in which the front maxillary teeth are grooved or perforated, another in which one or more of the hinder maxillary teeth are grooved, another in which all the teeth are solid. In the first the snakes are all poisonous, in the next they are doubtful or slightly poisonous, in the last they are harmless, and to it belong the only two British genera, *Tropidonotus* and *Coronella* (Plate xxix., 79, 80).

In the Viperidæ both jaws are toothed, but the only maxillary teeth are the poison fangs and their reserves. The teeth in the mandible are solid ; the fangs are perforated with a hole in front at the base connecting with the poison gland. The mandible has no coronoid ; the maxillary is short and thick, and erectile at a right angle to the transpalatine ; the quadrate is carried by the supratemporal, which is loosely attached to the top of the skull. The facial bones are movable. All the genera but one are viviparous. The only British genus is *Vipera* (Plate xxix., 81).

And now for the seven genera in alphabetical order :—

Anguis.   Plate xxviii. *LACERTILIA.*

75. *fragilis,*   SLOW-WORM.   No visible legs ; eyes with movable eyelids.

The Slow-worm, though frequently called the Blindworm, has a particularly bright little eye. The tongue is broad and notched, but not cleft or forked ; the teeth are small and slightly hooked, and are absent from the palate. The body and tail are covered with small rounded scales that look like faint markings, a ring of larger scales dividing off the tail from the body. The body is cylindrical, without a lateral fold, and of much the same diameter throughout. The skin is smooth—generally brownish-grey above, with rows of dark spots down the back and along the sides, and bluish-black with white reticulations below—and has a metallic lustre which gives the animal the appearance of a short round bar of tarnished copper. In length the Slow-worm may reach seventeen inches, but it does not often exceed twelve, more than half of which is tail. It is not a snake, it is not venomous, it is quite harmless to man, and when caught or alarmed becomes so rigid with fright that some of its tail is frequently broken off, to grow again, but not to the same length as before. It may frequently be noticed basking in the sun, a habit characteristic of the female a week or two before the eggs are brought forth in July, August, or September. The young make their escape from the eggs very soon after they are extruded. There are usually from ten to a dozen of them at a time, about an inch and a half long, white in colour, with a black streak down the middle of the back and a dark streak along each side. The food consists of small slugs, insects, and worms, the slugs being taken down head foremost, the worms being bitten into and sucked before they are swallowed. The Slow-worm feeds during the daytime, and at night shelters under stones and moss, or in a burrow of its own making, such as that in which, in company with others, it spends the winter. Though not met with in Iceland and Ireland, it ranges from Lapland to Western Asia and Algeria, and is still to be found on most of our wild, open commons away from water.

Anguis is not the only legless genus of lizards, nor are all the members of the same family without legs, for *Gerrhonotus* has both pairs well developed, and *Pseudopus* (the glass snakes) though without the front pair, has the hind pair represented by spikes. The Aniellidæ and Anelytropidæ are quite legless; the Dibamidæ and Pygopodidæ have no front legs and only a pair of flaps where the hind ones ought to be. The Amphisbænidæ have no legs, except in *Chirotes*, which has a short front pair with four digits. In the skinks (Scincidæ) almost every stage is represented, some being without fore legs, some without hind legs, some with one, two, three, four, or five digits, and some with mere conical stumps and no digits whatever.

Chelone. Plate xxvii. *THECOPHORA.*

73. *imbricata,* Hawksbill Turtle. Shell covered with horny plates; limbs paddle-shaped.

This is the turtle from which comes our tortoiseshell. It appears in the British list mainly owing to an unfortunate vagrant that was caught in the Severn, and lived for some months in Dr. Turton's father's fish-pond. When young the shell is serrated all round, but in time the front half becomes smooth. The shields overlap at first, but cease to do so in old age; the head is small and prominent, with the upper jaw curved over the lower so as to form a hooked beak; all the flippers have two claws. The shields and scales are dark brown with yellow edges. This turtle is less than a yard long. Unlike the only other member of the genus—*C. mydas*, the green turtle—it is entirely carnivorous and by no means wholesome.

Coronella. Plate xxix. *OPHIDIA.*

80. *lævis,* Smooth Snake. Scales smooth; head short and not markedly distinct from neck. A dark stripe through the eye.

The Smooth Snake is very local in Britain, it having been found as yet only in Hampshire, Dorsetshire, and, doubtfully, in south-western Surrey. It has teeth in both jaws, but no poison fangs. The lower maxillary teeth are equal in size, but those in the upper maxillary are larger at the back than in front, and do not exceed twenty in number. The rostral shield is as deep as it is broad, and is produced between the internasals. There are seven or eight labial plates, the third and fourth of which extend to the eye; the four lower labials touch the chin shields. The scales on the back are rhomboidal and smooth, and in nineteen rows ; the plates on the lower surface are rounded, those along the tail being in a double series. The tail is short, and strong at the base. The colour is reddish brown above, with a dark patch on the back of the head from which run two stripes or rows of dots along the body, and there is a dark stripe through the eye, often extending along the neck ; the lower parts are paler, but vary through almost every shade of brown, orange, grey, and pale blue. For a few days after casting the skin the ground colour is blue, but this soon fades into browns and dull reds. The young are brownish above, and pale, glittering blue below. They escape from the eggs almost while they are being laid, and for some time are protected by the mother. They have been described by Frank Buckland as basking in the sun, nestling on her coils, being then some five inches long, as thick as a goosequill, and smoother than the finest velvet. Though this snake has been caught bathing it seems to have no marked partiality for water, being generally met with in dry. sunny, stony places, where it feeds chiefly on mice and voles, and lizards, by preference, when it can get them. In length it is about two feet, the male being the smaller. It is fiercer in temper than the Ringed Snake, and does not hibernate for so long, but it does not range so far north, its area extending through Central and Southern Europe into Asia Minor.

Lacerta.   Plate xxviii.   *LACERTILIA*.

  76. *vivipara*,   VIVIPAROUS LIZARD. Tail less than twice as long as head and body ; foot longer than head ; under parts orange or yellow ; no palatal teeth.

  77. *agilis*,   SAND LIZARD. Tail less than twice as long as head and body ; foot not longer than head ; under parts greenish white ; palatal teeth.

  78. *viridis*,   GREEN LIZARD. Tail more than twice as long as head and body.

These three lizards live principally on flies and other insects and on worms and snails. On the skin of the head are large shields and small scales, and the scales on the back are smaller than those on the tail. The tail is long, round, pointed, and so brittle that it can easily be thrown off. There are five fingers and five toes, all with sharp claws, and all having warty plates on the under surface. The tongue is long, bifid, and papillose. The teeth are attached by their sides to the side of the jaw, and not by their bases to its ridge.

The Viviparous Lizard is from five to seven inches in length. Its head is depressed and the nose pointed ; there are no granules above the eyes, and the rostral shield is separated from the nostril. The collar is composed of seven or nine plates, and has a serrated edge. The scales on the back are long, narrow, hexagonal, and indistinctly keeled, and not larger than those in the sides ; the scales round the body do not exceed forty-five in number. The tail is cylindrical for half its length, and then begins to taper ; it is rather more than half as long again as the head and body. The fore leg is a third as long as the body, and the hind leg half as long. The upper parts are spotted olive brown or reddish, often with a black streak down the back, and a dark band, edged with yellowish, along the side; the underparts are spotted, those of the male being deep orange, those of the female yellow. The female is rather larger than the male, and not so high on the legs or long in the tail. The young are blackish; they escape from the egg as soon as it is extruded, but feed for a few days on its remains. On their first appearance they are barely three-quarters of an inch long, and seldom exceed a dozen in number. In a few days they begin to run about in pursuit of the aphides and other tiny insects on which for some time they feed. This species ranges across Europe and Asia from Ireland to Saghalien, and from seventy degrees north latitude to the northern slopes of the Alps and Pyrenees.

The Sand Lizard, otherwise the Grey Lizard, is larger, being about nine inches in length. Its head is short and the nose blunt; there are no granules above the eyes, and the rostral shield is separated from the nostril as in the foregoing species. The serrated collar is composed of from seven to eleven plates. The scales on the back are rounded or angular, and distinctly keeled; the scales round the body do not exceed fifty-eight in number. The tail is thick, and has from fifty to eighty rings of scales, and is about half as long again as the head and body. The ventral plates are in six or eight rows, of which the two in the middle are the narrowest. The fore leg is nearly a quarter as long as the body, and the hind leg about three-eighths as long. The upper parts are olive or sandy brown, the lower whitish green, generally with black spots. The male is greener in tint than the female, and both are streaked with spots and patches, the female having three rows of dark brown spots with white centres along the side. The male is a trifle smaller than the female, and has a proportionately longer tail. The young are greyish brown, with lines of white spots edged with black. The eggs, from five to eight in number, are laid in a hole in the sand, covered over, and left to be hatched by the sun's heat in July or August. This species ranges from the south of England into North-western Asia, being mostly confined to sandy heaths. Like the viviparous lizard, it is not met with south of the Alps or Pyrenees.

The Green Lizard is fifteen or sixteen inches in length. The nose is rather pointed, the rostral shield touches the nostril, and behind each nostril are two small scales. The serrated collar is made up of from seven to twelve plates, and is fairly conspicuous. The ventral plates are in six or eight rows, the second row from beneath being the largest. The scales round the body may be sixty-six in number; the scales on the tail are keeled. The tail is twice as long as the head and body; the fore leg is a quarter as long, and the hind leg two-thirds as long. In the males the hind leg is stouter than in the females, the tail is thicker at the base, the head is higher and larger, and the blue patch on the throat is broader and present at all seasons. In colour this lizard is green above, yellow below, the females, which are rather smaller in size, being browner than the males. Both are spotted with black, but the female's spots are edged with yellow, and the blue throat patch is not conspicuous and only appears during the breeding season. The young are pale brown with yellow streaks on the side. The eggs, from eight to eleven in number, are laid in the sand in June and hatched, by the sun's heat, in July. The Green Lizard is said to have been found in England; it certainly exists in Jersey, which brings it within the British fauna, its true home is in the rocky districts of Central and Southern Europe, whence it ranges into South-western Asia. Like our two other lizards it goes into winter quarters in October, and does not awake from its long sleep until spring is well advanced and the weather warm enough for its habits and its food. It is said to prefer butter-flies to flies and gnats, but really nothing small and alive in the animal way comes amiss to it and the others.

Sphargis.   Plate xxvii.   *ATHECA*.

74. *coriacea*,   LEATHERY TURTLE. No epidermal shields; carapace consisting of small plates covered with leathery skin.

This widely-distributed turtle has become British by being caught two or three times in British waters. It is interesting as being the only living representative of what used to be a rather extensive family. The carapace is continuous all round and' has a pointed end. In colour it is dark brown above with yellow spots, the legs and tail being black. The fore legs are twice as long as the hind legs; and it measures about six feet six in length. It is as often described under the generic name of *Dermochelys* as under that of *Sphargis*, but the latter is the older, and seems to have been given it for the noise the first specimen made when being killed. As a British animal its only habit worth noticing is that of blundering into a fishing net about once in a century and causing a considerable amount of damage and excitement.

Tropidonotus.   Plate xxix.   *OPHIDIA*.

79. *natrix*,   RINGED SNAKE. Black collar, frequently with a white or yellow one, more or less incomplete, in front of it.

The Common, Ringed or Grass Snake is found in England and Wales, but does not cross St. George's Channel or, apparently, the Tweed, though in Scandinavia it ranges up to the latitude of the Vigten Islands. It has teeth in both jaws, the maxillary teeth decreasing in length towards the front, those in the upper jaw being thirty or less in number. The scales on the back are oval, distinctly keeled, and in nineteen rows; the plates on the under surface are single and extend from side to side, those under the tail being in pairs. The head is ovate, depressed, and wider than the neck, and has seven upper labial shields, the third and fourth of which reach the aper-ture of the eye. The labials are white or yellowish. The colour above ranges from deep olive brown to pale greyish green, the under parts being white, speckled with black, and tinged with grey. On the back there are generally two parallel rows of blackish dots, and along the side there are black patches. In length this snake has been known to exceed six feet, but it is generally three feet or less, the female, as in all snakes, being the larger. The tail is a quarter as long as the body. The eggs are laid in July and August, in heaps of manure or decaying vegetable matter; they are usually from fifteen to twenty in number, but may be thirty or more, and are about an inch long, pale yellow in colour, obtuse at each end, and sticking together. They are hatched by the heat of the sun and the fermentation of their surroundings. The young feed on worms, tadpoles, and other soft animals, but as they grow up the food seems to consist mainly of frogs, newts, and fishes, so that they are seldom found far away from water or marshy ground. They dive after their prey, swim with their head and neck out of water, and take their rest coiled up in the water with their head held just above its surface. They cast their skin several times during the year, bursting it at the neck, and leaving it behind as they crawl out of it through thick herbage. They have no poison fangs and are quite harmless, but when handled they emit a most noisome odour that may be due to fright or a means of defence in the method of the skunk. It should be clearly understood that a snake's " fang " is a tooth, and not the tongue, which in this species is forked to a third of its length. Hibernation begins in October and lasts for some four months, and occasionally parties collect and sleep together coiled up in the same hole. The distribution of this snake extends from Central Europe into Algeria and Central Asia, and it varies a good deal in colour in the outlying regions of its area.

Vipera.   Plate xxix.   *OPHIDIA*.

81. *berus,*   VIPER. Scales keeled ; labial shields separated from the eye by scales ; zigzag line down back.

The Viper, otherwise the Adder, ranges all over Britain, from Caithness to Cornwall, and all across Europe and Asia, its easterly limit being the island of Saghalien ; in the north it reaches the Arctic Circle, but it does not go further south than Central Spain. Like the Ringed Snake it is absent from Ireland. It is our only venomous serpent, and can be identified by its having a row of teeth only in the lower jaw, those in the upper jaw consisting only of the two poison fangs and their reserves. These fangs are curved, and have a slit near the tip communicating with the tube through the tooth down which the poison is squirted from the gland at the side of the head when the strike is made. When not in use the fangs are kept folded backwards in a groove in the gum, and when broken off they are replaced from the reserves. The body scales are distinctly keeled and in twenty-one rows. The head is covered with small scales and a few shields. The labial shields are separated from the eye by one or two series of scales. The upper, six to ten in number, are whitish or yellowish ; the lower labials, numbering from three to five, are in contact with the chin shields. There is no pit between the nostrils and the eye. The colour varies from ashy grey, through reddish brown to black, the end of the tail being frequently yellow or red. The back has a broad zigzag stripe more or less noticeable ; the head has the " death's head," formed by bars across a sort of broad arrow pointing forwards from the nape, and there is a dark streak ending in the eye. The males are lighter in colour but have darker markings; the female is larger than the male. The length may reach twenty-eight inches, but in this country the average is ten. The tail is about a seventh of the total length in the male and about a tenth in the female. The female has a habit of basking in the sun, apparently for the purpose of stimulating the development of the eggs, which are extruded in July and August, the young, from ten to twenty in number, escaping from them at the same time. As Gilbert White says, "they issue into the world with the true viper spirit about them, showing great alertness as soon as disengaged." Though frequently seen abroad in the daytime, vipers are chiefly nocturnal. They live largely on mice and voles, and hence are found in the fields of grain on which those rodents feed. They do not enter water, and prefer sunny, open places, heaths and moors, and the outskirts and clearings of the woods. They hibernate, often in company, for nearly half the year, but occasionally emerge from their retreat if the weather be warmer than usual. They cast their skin once or oftener during the summer, and for a few days afterwards are quite brilliant in colour. To prepare for striking a viper coils itself up with its head in the centre of the coil and drawn a little back, and quick as lightning uncoils itself like a spring, supporting itself on its tail, and distending its mouth upwards, drops its fangs forwards and drives them straight into the victim, closing the mouth as the blow is given so as to squirt the venom into the wound. The bite is but momentary, the fangs being withdrawn as soon as the injection is made, ready for a second attack if necessary. A viper can, however, strike without coiling, and should never be held by the tail or the middle, but always near the head. As there are two poison teeth, there are, of course, two holes in the flesh which are the width of the mouth apart. The poisoning does not always end fatally, but it is as well to avoid it if possible. In the New Forest, where more vipers have been caught than elsewhere, the professional hunters use a forked stick about five feet long with which to pin the reptile down to the ground by its neck, and carry a pair of wooden pincers with points half an inch broad with which to lift it safely into the collecting box.

In these notes we have said nothing about the many synonyms borne by these reptiles, but, as a help to reference, we may as well give a selection from these alternative names, some of which are of recent introduction, while others are more or less obsolete.

Anguis bicolor, 75	Chelonia multiscutata, 73
Anguis cinereus, 75	Coluber austriacus, 80
Anguis eryx, 75	Coluber berus, 81
Anguis fragilis, 75	Coluber cœruleus, 81
Anguis lineata, 75	Coluber ferrugineus, 80
	Coluber lævis, 80
Caretta imbricata, 3	Coluber murorum, 79
Caretta squamata, 73	Coluber natrix, 79
Chelone imbricata, 73	Coluber torquatus, 79
Chelonia imbricata, 73	Coriudo coriacea, 74

Coronella austriaca, 80
Coronella lævis, 89

Dermatochelys atlantica, 74
Dermatochelys coriacea, 74
Dermatochelys porcata, 74
Dermochelys coriacea, 74

Eretmochelys squamata, 73

Lacerta ædura, 76
Lacerta agilis, 76, 77
Lacerta arenicola, 77
Lacerta bilineata, 78
Lacerta bistriata 78
Lacerta catenata, 77
Lacerta chloronota, 78
Lacerta chrysogaster, 76
Lacerta crocea, 76
Lacerta elegans, 78
Lacerta europæa, 77
Lacerta montana, 76
Lacerta nigra, 76
Lacerta practicola, 76
Lacerta rosea, 77
Lacerta sepium, 77
Lacerta smaragdina, 78
Lacerta stirpium, 77
Lacerta varius, 78
Lacerta viridis, 78
Lacerta vivipara, 76
Lacerta vulgaris, 77

Natrix dumfrisiensis, 80
Natrix torquata, 79
Natrix vulgaris, 79

Pelias berus, 81

Sphargis coriacea, 74
Sphargis mercurii, 74
Seps argus, 77
Seps cœrulescens, 77
Seps ruber, 77
Seps stellatus, 77
Seps terrestris, 78
Seps varius, 77

Testudo caretta, 73
Testudo coriacea, 74
Testudo imbricata, 73
Testudo lyra, 74
Testudo mercurii, 74
Testudo tuberculata, 74
Tropidonotus natrix, 79
Tropidonotus persa, 79

Vipera berus, 81
Vipera communis, 81
Vipera vulgaris, 81

Zootoca muralis, 76
Zootoca vivipara, 76

The fossil reptiles of the British area at present known are nearly four hundred in number. The oldest genus is *Protorosaurus*, represented by two species in the Permian Marl Slate, and reptilian remains have been collected from every succeeding formation up to the Oligocene. In the Trias we have *Palæosaurus* and *Rhyncosaurus*, and, amongst others, that most curious form *Elginia*, in which the skull has so many protuberances and the third eye is so clearly shown on the top of the head. In the Rhætics are three Plesiosaurs—their first appearance—the Ichthyosaurs and Steneosaurs beginning in the Lias. The Oolites have yielded three Cetiosaurs, ten Cimoliosaurs, seven Ichthyosaurs, all the nine Pliosaurs, and one species of Pterodactyl, and three of the allied genus *Rhamphorhynchus*, besides representatives of some two dozen other genera. From the Purbecks have come, in addition to the ten genera of mammals, about seventeen genera of reptiles, among them the oldest turtle, *Chelone obovata*. In the Wealden the reptilian genera are almost as numerous, the most familiar being, perhaps, Iguanodon. The Cretaceous rocks are also rich in reptiles, among them being the sea-serpents, *Mosasaurus*, *Dolichosaurus*, and *Leiodon*.

With the Upper Chalk the era of the monster reptiles closes, the fauna of the Eocene being of a much more modern type. Here we have a crocodile, and a garial, eight soft-shelled turtles of the existing genus *Trionyx*, nine hard-shelled turtles (*Argillochelys*, *Lytoloma*, *Thalassochelys*), a pond tortoise (*Emys comptoni*), a leathery turtle (*Eosphargis*), two lizards, one (*Lacerta eocena*) of the same genus as that now represented in the area, the other (*Iguana europæa*) of a genus now only known in Tropical America ; an early relative of the slow worm (*Placosaurus*), and three sea snakes (*Palæophis*) as large as the largest pythons. No reptiles have as yet been found in the Pliocene, but the Forest Bed has yielded three, all existing, these being *Tropidonotus natrix*, the ringed snake, *Vipera berus*, the viper, and *Emys orbicularis*, the European pond-tortoise, not now living in this country, but ranging from Central Europe into Algeria and Asia Minor. This tortoise, as will be seen from the following list, is the only reptile discovered up to now in our Pleistocene, which is almost as remarkable as that no remains of reptiles or amphibians should have been found in our caves or river deposits.

As we gave a list of our mammals extinct and extant, we cannot very well avoid giving one of the reptiles on the same plan, though it is rather a heavy undertaking, and will occupy more space than we can well spare. However, here we have it as complete as we can make it :—

BRITISH REPTILES PAST AND PRESENT.

CROCODILIA.

CROCODILIDÆ.

> Diplocynodon hantoniensis (Upper Eocene).
> Ornithostoma (Cambridge Greensand).
> Crocodilus cantabrigiensis (Cambridge Greensand).
> Crocodilus icenicus (Cambridge Greensand).
> Crocodilus spenceri (Lower Eocene).
> Garialis dixoni (Middle Eocene).
> Heterosuchus valdensis (Wealden).

GONIOPHILIDÆ.

> Hylæochampsa vectianus (Wealden).
> Theriosuchus pusillus (Middle Purbeck).
> Goniophilis carinata (Wealden).
> Goniophilis crassidens (Wealden).
> Goniophilis simus (Middle Purbeck).
> Goniophilis tenuidens (Middle Purbeck).
> Nannosuchus gracilidens (Middle Purbeck).
> Oweniasuchus major (Middle Purbeck).
> Oweniasuchus minor (Middle Purbeck).

Pholidosaurus meyeri (Wealden).
Petrosuchus lævidens (Middle Purbeck).
Suchosaurus cultridens (Wealden).

TELEOSAURIDÆ.

Dacosaurus maximus (Kimeridge Clay).
Metriorhynchus gracile (Portlandian).
Metriorhynchus hastifer (Portlandian).
Metriorhynchus moreli (Oxford Clay).
Metriorhynchus palpebrosum (Kimeridge Clay).
Metriorhynchus superciliosum (Oxford Clay).
Steneosaurus bollensis (Upper Lias).
Steneosaurus boutilieri (Great Oolite).
Steneosaurus brevidens (Great Oolite).
Steneosaurus brevior (Upper Lias).
Steneosaurus chapmani (Upper Lias).
Steneosaurus geoffroyi (Great Oolite).
Steneosaurus laticeps (Great Oolite).
Steneosaurus latifrons (Upper Lias).
Steneosaurus megarhinus (Kimeridge Clay).
Steneosaurus megistorhynchus (Inferior Oolite).
Steneosaurus purbeckensis (Purbeck).
Steneosaurus stephani (Cornbrash).
Steneosaurus temporalis (Great Oolite).
Teleosaurus asthenodeirus (Kimeridge Clay).
Teleosaurus geoffroyi (Stonesfield Slate).
Teleosaurus subulidens (Stonesfield Slate).

PHYTOSAURIDÆ.

Stagonolepis robertsoni (Keuper).
Dasygnathus longidens (Keuper).

DINOSAURIA.

SAUROPODA.

CETIOSAURIDÆ.

Cardiodon rugulosus (Forest Marble).
Titanosaurus (Wealden and Upper Greensand).
Pleurocœlus valdensis (Wealden).
Dinodocus mackesoni (Lower Greensand).
Cetiosaurus brachyurus (Wealden).
Cetiosaurus glymptonensis (Forest Marble).
Cetiosaurus longus (Lower Oolite).
Cetiosaurus oxoniensis (Great Oolite and Forest Marble).
Morosaurus brevis (Wealden).
Craterosaurus pottonensis (Wealden).

ATLANTOSAURIDÆ.

Pelorosaurus conybearei (Wealden).
Pelorosaurus humerocristatus (Portlandian).
Ornithopsis hulkei (Wealden).
Ornithopsis humerocristatus (Kimeridge Clay).
Ornithopsis leedsi (Oxford Clay).
Ornithopsis manseli (Kimeridge Clay).
Gigantosaurus megalonyx (Kimeridge Clay).
Macrurosaurus semnus (Cambridge Greensand).
Hoplosaurus armatus (Wealden).
Palæosaurus cylindrodon (Keuper).
Palæosaurus stricklandi (Rhætic).
Thecospondylus horneri (Wealden).

Theropoda.

CŒLURIDÆ.

Cœlurus daviesi (Wealden).
Calamospondylus foxi (Wealden).

MEGALOSAURIDÆ.

Aristosuchus pusillus (Wealden).
Megalosaurus bucklandi (Inferior Oolite).
Megalosaurus insignis (Kimeridge Clay).
Megalosaurus oweni (Wealden).
Bothriospondylus robustus (Forest Marble).
Bothriospondylus suffosus (Kimeridge Clay).
Cladyodon lloydi (Keuper).
Zanclodon cambrensis (Rhætic).
Sarcolestes leedsi (Oxford Clay).

ANCHISAURIDÆ.

Thecodontosaurus antiquus (Keuper).
Thecodontosaurus platyodon (Keuper).

Ornithopoda.

OMOSAURIDÆ.

Omosaurus armatus (Kimeridge Clay).
Omosaurus durobrivensis (Oxford Clay).
Omosaurus hastiger (Kimeridge Clay).

SCELIDOSAURIDÆ.

Scelidosaurus harrisoni (Lower Lias).
Acanthopholis eucercus (Cambridge Greensand)

Acanthopholis horridus (Chalk Marl).
Acanthopholis platypus (Cambridge Greensand).
Acanthopholis stereocercus (Cambridge Greensand).
Regnosaurus northamptoni (Wealden).
Hylæosaurus armatus (Wealden).
Priodontognathus phillipsi (Cambridge Greensand).
Anoplosaurus curtonotus (Cambridge Greensand).
Anoplosaurus major (Cambridge Greensand).
Eucercosaurus tanyspondylus (Cambridge Greensand).
Vectisaurus valdensis (Wealden).
Syngonosaurus macrocercus (Cambridge Greensand).
Polacanthus foxi (Wealden).

IGUANODONTIDÆ.

Hypsilophodon foxi (Wealden).
Camptosaurus leedsi (Oxford Clay).
Camptosaurus prestwichi (Kimeridge Clay).
Camptosaurus valdensis (Wealden).
Cryptodraco eumerus (Oxford Clay).
Iguanodon bernissartensis (Wealden).
Iguanodon dawsoni (Wealden).
Iguanodon fittoni (Wealden).
Iguanodon hollingtoniensis (Wealden).
Iguanodon mantelli (Wealden).
Iguanodon phillipsi (Wealden).
Sphenospondylus gracilis (Wealden).

TRACHODONTIDÆ.

Trachodon cantabrigiensis (Cambridge Greensand).
Echinodon becklesi (Middle Purbeck).
Nuthetes destructor (Middle Purbeck).

ORNITHOSAURIA.

PTEROSAURIA.

Ornithocheirus brachyrhinus (Cambridge Greensand).
Ornithocheirus capito (Cambridge Greensand).
Ornithocheirus clavirostris (Wealden).
Ornithocheirus clifti (Wealden).
Ornithocheirus colorhinus (Cambridge Greensand).
Ornithocheirus compressirostris (Lower Chalk).
Ornithocheirus crassidens (Cambridge Greensand).
Ornithocheirus curtus (Wealden).
Ornithocheirus cuvieri (Lower Chalk).
Ornithocheirus daviesi (Gault).
Ornithocheirus dentatus (Cambridge Greensand).

1

Ornithocheirus denticulatus (Cambridge Greensand).
Ornithocheirus diomedius (Chalk).
Ornithocheirus enchorhynchus (Cambridge Green-
sand).
Ornithocheirus eurygnathus (Cambridge Greensand).
Ornithocheirus fittoni (Cambridge Greensand).
Ornithocheirus giganteus (Lower Chalk).
Ornithocheirus huxleyi (Cambridge Greensand).
Ornithocheirus machærorhynchus (Cambridge Green-
sand).
Ornithocheirus microdon (Cambridge Greensand).
Ornithocheirus nasutus (Cambridge Greensand).
Ornithochierus nobilis (Wealden).
Ornithocheirus oweni (Cambridge Greensand).
Ornithocheirus oxyrhinus (Cambridge Greensand).
Ornithocheirus platystomus (Cambridge Greensand).
Ornithocheirus polyodon (Cambridge Greensand).
Ornithocheirus reedi (Cambridge Greensand).
Ornithocheirus scaphorhynchus (Cambridge Green-
sand).
Ornithocheirus sedgwicki (Cambridge Greensand).
Ornithocheirus simus (Cambridge Greeensand).
Ornithocheirus tenuirostris (Cambridge Greensand).
Ornithocheirus xyphorhynchus (Cambridge Green-
sand).
Doratorhynchus longicollis (Lower Chalk).
Scaphognathus purdoni (Upper Lias).
Rhamphocephalus bucklandi (Stonesfield Slate).
Rhamphocephalus depressirostris (Stonesfield Slate).
Rhamphocephalus prestwichi (Stonesfield Slate).
Dimorphodon macroynx (Lower Lias).
Pterodactylus pleydelli (Kimeridge Clay).
Pterodactylus sagittirostris (Wealden).

PTERANODONTIA.

Ornithostoma (Cambridge Greensand).

CHELONIA.

TRIONYCHIDÆ.

Trionyx barbaræ (Upper Eocene).
Trionyx bowerbanki (Middle Eocene).
Trionyx circumsulcatus (Upper Eocene).
Trionyx henrici (Upper Eocene).
Trionyx incrassatus (Upper Eocene).
Trionyx planus (Upper Eocene).
Trionyx pustulatus (Lower Eocene).
Trionyx rivosus (Upper Eocene).

CHELONIDÆ.

Cimoliochelys benstedi (Lower Chalk).
Chelone hoffmanni (Chalk).
73. Chelone imbricata (Existent), Hawk's-Bill Turtle.
Chelone jessoni (Cambridge Greensand).
Chelone obovata (Purbeck).
Argillochelys antiqua (Lower Eocene).
Argillochelys convexa (Lower Eocene).
Argillochelys cuneiceps (Lower Eocene).
Argillochelys subcristata (Middle Eocene).
Thallassochelys eocænica (Middle Eocene).
Lytoloma cantabrigiense (Cambridge Greensand).
Lytoloma crassicostatum (Lower Eocene).
Lytoloma longiceps (Lower Eocene).
Lytoloma planimentum (Lower Eocene).
Lytoloma trigoniceps (Middle Eocene).

TESTUDINIDÆ.

Testudo cantabrigiensis (Cambridge Greensand).
Emys comptoni (Lower Eocene).
Emys orbicularis (Forest Bed, Pleistocene, and Existent in Central Europe), European Pond Tortoise.
Ocadia crassa (Upper Eocene).
Ocadia oweni (Upper Eocene).
Chrysemys bicarinata (Lower Eocene).
Chrysemys testudiniformis (Lower Eocene).
Protemys serrata (Lower Greensand).

DERMATEMYDIDÆ.

Trachyaspis hantoniensis (Upper Eocene).

CHELYDRIDÆ.

Tretosternum bakewelli (Wealden).
Tretosternum punctatum (Wealden).
Anosteira anglica (Upper Eocene).
Pseudotrionyx delheidi (Lower Eocene).

ACICHELYIDÆ.

Thalassemys longii (Kimeridge Clay).
Thalassemys ruetimeyeri (Purbeck).
Pelobatochelys blakei (Kimeridge Clay).
Tropidemys langi (Kimeridge Clay).

PELOMEDUSIDÆ.

Podocnemis bowerbanki (Lower Eocene).
Podocnemis delabechei (Lower Eocene).
Dacochelys delabechei (Lower Eocene).
Rhinochelys brachyrhina (Cambridge Greensand).
Rhinochelys cantabrigiensis (Cambridge Greensand).
Rhinochelys elegans (Gault).
Rhinochelys jessoni (Cambridge Greensand).
Rhinochelys macrorhina (Cambridge Greensand).
Rhinochelys pulchriceps (Cambridge Greensand).

PLESIOCHELYIDÆ.

Hylæochelys belli (Wealden).
Hylæochelys emarginata (Purbeck).
Hylæochelys lata (Upper Greensand).
Hylæochelys latiscutata (Wealden).
Plesiochelys brodiei (Wealden).
Plesiochelys valdensis (Wealden).
Platemys (Wealden).

PLEUROSTERNIDÆ.

Pleurosternum bullocki (Purbeck).
Pleurosternum oweni (Purbeck).
Pleurosternum portlandicum (Portlandian).
Pleurosternum sedgwicki (Purbeck).
Pleurosternum typocardium (Purbeck).
Pleurosternum vansittarti (Purbeck).
Platychelys anglica (Middle Purbeck).
Archæochelys valdensis (Wealden).
Protochelys stricklandi (Stonesfield Slate).

SPHARGIDÆ.

Psephophorus (Middle Eocene).
Eosphargis gigas (Lower Eocene).
74. Sphargis coriacea (Existent), Leathery Turtle.

PROTOSTEGIDÆ.

Protostega anglica (Cambridge Greensand).
Psephoderma anglicum (Rhætic).
Stegochelys planiceps (Portlandian).

SAUROPTERYGIA.

PLESIOSAURIDÆ.

Pliosaurus brachydeirus (Kimeridge Clay).
Pliosaurus brachyspondylus (Kimeridge Clay).
Pliosaurus evansi (Oxford Clay).
Pliosaurus ferox (Oxford Clay).
Pliosaurus gamma (Oxford Clay).
Pliosaurus grossouvrei (Coral Rag).
Pliosaurus macromerus (Kimeridge Clay).
Pliosaurus nitidus (Kimeridge Clay).
Pliosaurus simplex (Kimeridge Clay).
Peloneustes æqualis (Kimeridge Clay).
Peloneustes philarchus (Oxford Clay).
Thaumatosaurus arcuatus (Lower Lias).
Thaumatosaurus carinatus (Kimeridge Clay)·
Thaumatosaurus cramptoni (Upper Lias).
Thaumatosaurus megacephalus (Lower Lias).
Thaumatosaurus propinquus (Middle Lias).
Thaumatosaurus zetlandicus (Upper Lias).
Polyptychodon continuus (Cretaceous).
Polyptychodon interruptus (Cretaceous).
Cimoliosaurus bernardi (Cretaceous).
Cimoliosaurus brachistospondylus (Kimeridge Clay).
Cimoliosaurus brevior (Cornbrash and Kimeridge Clay).
Cimoliosaurus cantabrigiensis (Cretaceous).
Cimoliosaurus constrictus (Cretaceous).
Cimoliosaurus durobrivensis (Oxford Clay).
Cimoliosaurus erraticus (Stonesfield Slate).
Cimoliosaurus eurymerus (Oxford Clay).
Cimoliosaurus latispinus (Lower Greensand).
Cimoliosaurus limnophilus (Wealden).
Cimoliosaurus oxoniensis (Oxford Clay).
Cimoliosaurus planus (Cambridge Greensand).
Cimoliosaurus plicatus (Oxford Clay and Portlandian).
Cimoliosaurus portlandicus (Portlandian).
Cimoliosaurus richardsoni (Oxford Clay).
Cimoliosaurus smithi (Cretaceous).
Cimoliosaurus trochanterius (Oxford Clay and Kimeridge Clay).
Eretmosaurus macropterus (Upper Lias).
Eretmosaurus rugosus (Lower Lias).
Plesiosaurus bitractensis (Rhætic).
Plesiosaurus compressus (Lias).
Plesiosaurus conybearei (Lower Lias).
Plesiosaurus costatus (Rhætic).
Plesiosaurus depressicostatus (Lias ?).
Plesiosaurus eleutheraxon (Lower Lias).
Plesiosaurus ellipsospondylus (Cambridge Greensand.)

Plesiosaurus hawkinsi (Lower Lias).
Plesiosaurus homalospondylus (Upper Lias)
Plesiosaurus leptopleuron (Lias ?).
Plesiosaurus longirostris (Lias).
Plesiosaurus macrocephalus (Lower Lias).
Plesiosaurus macromus (Lias).
Plesiosaurus megapleuron (Lias ?).
Plesiosaurus pectopleuron (Oxford Clay ?).
Plesiosaurus rostratus (Lower Lias).
Plesiosaurus subconcavus (Lias).
Plesiosaurus subplanus (Oxford Clay ?).
Plesiosaurus subtrigonus (Lower Lias).
Plesiosaurus trigonus (Rhætic).

SAURIA.

DOLICHOSAURIDÆ.

Saurospondylus dissimilis (Lower Chalk).
Dolichosaurus longicollis (Lower Chalk).

IGUANIDÆ.

Iguana europæa (Upper Eocene).

ANGUIDÆ.

Placosaurus margariticeps (Upper Eocene).
75. Anguis fragilis (Existent), Slow Worm.

LACERTIDÆ.

76. Lacerta vivipara (Existent), Viviparous Lizard.
77. Lacerta agilis (Existent), Sand Lizard.
78. Lacerta viridis (Existent), Green Lizard.
Lacerta eocena (Lower Eocene).
Conisaurus crassidens (Chalk).
Macellodus brodiei (Middle Purbeck).

COLUBRIDÆ.

79. Tropidonotus natrix (Forest Bed and Existent), Ringed Snake.
80. Coronella lævis (Existent), Smooth Snake.

VIPERIDÆ.

81. Vipera berus (Forest Bed and Existent), Viper.

PYTHONIDÆ.

Paleryx depressus (Upper Eocene).
Paleryx rhombifer (Upper Eocene).

PALÆOPHIDÆ.

Palæophis longus (Lower Eocene).
Palæophis toliapicus (Lower Eocene).
Palæophis typhæus (Lower Eocene).

MOSASAURIDÆ.

Leiodon anceps (Upper Chalk).
Platecarpus (Chalk).
Mosasaurus (Chalk).
Patricosaurus merocratus (Cambridge Greensand).

ICTHYOSAURIA.

ICTHYOSAURIDÆ.

Baptanodon cantabrigiensis (Cambridge Greensand).
Ophthalmosaurus icenicus (Oxford Clay and Kime-
ridge Clay).
Icthyosaurus acutirostris (Upper Lias).
Icthyosaurus æqualis (Kimeridge Clay).
Icthyosaurus breviceps (Lower Lias).
Icthyosaurus campylodon (Cretaceous).
Icthyosaurus communis (Lower Lias).
Icthyosaurus coniformis (Lower Lias).
Icthyosaurus conybearei (Lower Lias).
Icthyosaurus dilatatus (Oxford Clay).
Icthyosaurus entheciodon (Oxford Clay and Kime
ridge Clay).
Icthyosaurus intermedius (Lower Lias).
Icthyosaurus latifrons (Lower Lias).
Icthyosaurus megalodeirus (Oxford Clay).
Icthyosaurus ovalis (Kimeridge Clay).
Icthyosaurus platyodon (Lower Lias).
Icthyosaurus tenuirostris (Lower Lias).
Icthyosaurus thyreospondylus (Kimeridge Clay).
Icthyosaurus trigonodon (Upper Lias).
Icthyosaurus trigonus (Kimeridge Clay).
Icthyosaurus zetlandicus (Upper Lias).
Cetarthrosaurus walkeri (Cambridge Greensand)

RHYNCOCEPHALIA.

Telerpeton elginense (Keuper).
Rhynchosaurus articeps (Keuper).
Hyperodapedon gordoni (Keuper).

PROTOROSAURIA.

Protorosaurus huxleyi (Permian).
Protorosaurus speneri (Permian).

ANOMODONTIA.

Dicynodon (Keuper).
Elginia mirabilis (Keuper).
Gordonia duffiana (Keuper).
Geikia elginensis (Keuper).
Gordonia huxleyana (Keuper).
Gordonia juddiana (Keuper).
Gordonia traquairi (Keuper).

CHAPTER VIII.

THE BRITISH AMPHIBIANS.

———◆———

THERE are seven species of living British amphibians, three with tails and four without. The tailed ones are the newts, the tailless are the frogs and toads. The toads (*Bufo*) have no teeth; the frogs (*Rana*) have teeth in the upper jaw. The toads are warty on the under parts, and covered with warty protuberances on the upper parts; the frogs, though they may occasionally have a few warts on the upper parts, are always smooth below. This gives us—

ECAUDATA—

   1 (Ranidæ)—

      Teeth in upper jaw; skin of under parts smooth. *Rana*, 82, 83.

   2 (Bufonidæ)—

      Jaws toothless; skin of under parts warty. *Bufo*, 84, 85.

To which we may add—

CAUDATA—

   (Salamandridæ)—

      Tail flattened laterally and as long as body. *Triton*, 86 to 88.

And thus complete the list.

Here again we have enough for our purpose of identification, so far as our fauna is concerned, but something more formal and detailed is desirable. To begin with—What are amphibians? Amphibians are cold-blooded vertebrates in which the body is naked or has the scales imbedded in the skin. With a few exceptions they undergo a metamorphosis, during the early stages of which they are aquatic. As a rule they breathe by gills when young and by lungs when mature, but some retain their gills throughout life, and some never breathe by gills although they are present in the embryo Their skull articulates with the backbone by two condyles, which in a few cases are absent. There are no sternal ribs and no true sternum. The limbs, when present, are four in number and have distinct digits. When fins are present they are without fin-rays. They are divided into two sub-classes, one of which, Stegocephali, consists entirely of extinct species in which the head was protected by bony shields, the other, Lissamphibia, comprises those that have no such protection. Of these there are three orders, Ecaudata, Caudata, and Apoda. Of the last, or limbless Amphibians, we have no representative.

The Ecaudata have no tail when adult. They have four limbs. The body is short ; there are only eight, sometimes only seven, pre-sacral vertebræ. The frontal bones coalesce with the parietals, the radius coalesces with the ulna, the tibia coalesces with the fibula. The hind legs have an additional segment owing to the elongation of the astragalus and calcaneum in the metatarsus. There are two sub-orders, Aglossa and Phaneroglossa, the Aglossa being distin-guished by the absence of a tongue. The Phaneroglossa are divided into two series, Firmisternia and Arcifera, in the first of which the ventral halves of the shoulder girdle abut against each other and are firmly held by cartilage, while in the second the coracoid and pre-coracoid on each side diverge and are joined by curved cartilages which overlap each other. Of the Firmisternia the only British family is Ranidæ (the frogs), the Arcifera being represented by Bufonidæ (toads).

The Ranidæ have teeth in the upper jaw. There are no ribs. The vertebræ are concave in front, and the transverse processes of the sacral vertebra are either cylindrical or very slightly dilated. The precoracoids are parallel with the coracoids and are ossified from the clavicles. The only British genus is *Rana* (Plate xxx., 82, 83).

The Bufonidæ have no teeth in either jaw. There are no ribs. The vertebræ are procœlous, and the transverse processes of the sacral vertebra are distinctly dilated. The precoracoids are in contact with the coracoids at their outer ends and diverge towards the middle, where they are joined to them by the arched epicoracoid cartilage.

The Caudata have a tail throughout life. They have generally four, but in some cases only two limbs. The body is long and like that of a lizard, or that of an eel. The frontal bones do not coalesce with the parietals, nor do the palatines coalesce with the maxillaries. The radius is distinct from the ulna, and the tibia from the fibula. The vertebræ are concave behind—sometimes, as in the British genus, concave at both ends—and carry short ribs. There are four families. In one, Sirenidæ, the jaws are toothless and there are no hind legs. The others have teeth in both jaws and all four legs. In one, Proteidæ, there are no maxillaries ; both the other two have these upper jawbones but one, Amphiumidæ is distinguished from the other by having no eyelids. The fourth family, Salamandridæ, is the only one on our list.

In the Salamandridæ there are no gills in the adult state; there are always two pairs of limbs however small they may be; there are teeth in both jaws; there are maxillaries; and there are movable eyelids (except in one genus in which the animals are blind). The only British genus is *Triton* (Plates xxxii., xxxiii., 86 to 88).

It will be convenient for reference to deal with the genera in alphabetical order, as we have done in the case of the mammals and reptiles, although we have only three on our list.

Bufo. Plate xxxi. *ECAUDATA.*

84. *vulgaris,* COMMON TOAD. Brownish; no yellow stripe down back.

85. *calamita,* NATTERJACK. Greenish; yellow stripe down back.

Toads have no teeth in either jaw. Their limbs are shorter and thicker than those of the frogs, and placed further forwards on the body. The toes are short and webbed, but not so much so as a frog's, and their whole appearance is that of animals more adapted for crawling and walking than for leaping and swimming. The eggs are not laid in shapeless masses like those of the frog, but in two double rows or strings, which look like glass tubes filled with black beads. These strings, which are hung on to plants in the water, sometimes reach fifteen feet in length in the case of the common toad, those of the natterjack being half as long, and they swell up until they are about a quarter of an inch in diameter. The tadpoles emerge from the protecting jelly in from ten days to a fortnight, and for a few days hang on its remains, leaving them for the stems and leaves of water-plants, to which they cling by the sucker under their throats. They are then about half an inch long, and grow fast as their external gills begin to shrink. Some six weeks after attaining their freedom the hind legs appear, and in another three weeks the fore-limbs are protruded. Soon afterwards the tail is gradually absorbed, but not entirely so until after the toad has abandoned the water, to which, when mature, it returns every year for breeding purposes in the middle of April. The young of the natterjack are, in all stages, much smaller than those of the common species.

Toads feed on insects, snails, and earthworms, the worms being caught in the middle and cleaned between the fingers as they are stowed away into the mouth. They are generally busy after rain and towards evening, and have often been observed hunting in their leisurely way on moonlight nights. They are "excellent for beetles," by beetles meaning cockroaches, but it is not everyone who considers a toad's appearance prepossessing enough to have it in the house. Dirty as they look they are really very clean, and change their skin every few weeks by peeling it off and eating it. The new skin is at first of a lighter colour than the old one, and the male is generally rather smarter than the female. The Toad hibernates away from water in a hollow tree or in a hole in the ground, but does not live for centuries in solid rock, neither does it spit fire or venom, and it has no jewel in its head, unless the jewel be its eye.

The Common Toad may attain five inches in length. Its body is thick and tumid, the head large, with the crown flat, the muzzle short and rounded, the gape wide, the tongue not notched. There is a slight protuberance over each eye, and a larger one behind it. The iris is red, mottled with black. The hind legs are as long as, or rather longer than, the body. The third finger is the longest, the first being equal in length to the second and longer than the fourth. The male is smaller than the female, and can be identified by the brushes on the fingers. In colour this species is brown of all shades on the upper parts and whitish, occasionally tinged with pink, below. It ranges into Northern Africa and across Asia to Japan, but, unlike the natterjack, does not seem to have settled in Ireland.

The Natterjack seldom exceeds three inches in length. In general appearance it resembles the foregoing, but is a trifle less clumsily built. The eyes are more projecting, the eyelids more elevated, and the protuberance on the side of the head is smaller. The iris is greenish yellow and speckled. The hind legs are not so long as the body. The third finger is the longest, the first being equal in length to the second and shorter than the fourth. The male is of the same size as the female, and can be identified by the brushes on the fingers. The upper parts are greenish yellow with green spots, and a narrow yellow stripe is generally, but not always, present down the middle of the head and back. The whitish underparts are frequently speckled with black. This species is of somewhat active habits, and on occasion can break into the unmistakable run which in some districts has gained it the name of "the running toad." It is principally met with in Western Europe, from the south of Scotland to the Straits of Gibraltar, and has been recorded from Roscrea in Ireland.

Rana.   Plate xxx.   *ECAUDATA.*

82.   *temporaria,*   COMMON FROG.   Temples black ; hinder part of thighs unspotted.

83.   *esculenta,*   EDIBLE FROG.   Temples grey ; hinder part of thighs spotted.

The Frogs have teeth in the upper jaw as well as on the palate, the tongue is notched and free behind, the fingers are free and the toes webbed, and the fourth and fifth metatarsals diverge and are webbed together. The hind legs are more than half as long again as the body.

Frogs appear in several transition forms in their progress to maturity. The eggs are laid within small spheres of jelly which sink to the bottom of the water, and there begin to swell until they are buoyant enough to rise to the surface in a mass four or more inches across. The gelatinous wrapper preserves the eggs and embryos from injury, and often encloses algæ, which may help in aeration during the fortnight or so the embryo is enclosed within it. When the tiny tadpole leaves the protective coating it has external gills and a horse-shoe shaped sucker on the under side of the head with which it clings to water-plants and other objects. Then the depression in the front of the head deepens and opens into the alimentary canal, thus becoming the mouth with which the tadpole feeds on vegetable matter. As the locomotive powers improve, the sucker splits into two and is gradually disused. The external gills are soon replaced by an internal set enclosed in chambers, by the growth of the folds of which they are eventually closed in, with the exception of an aperture on the left side through which the water taken in by the mouth is ejected after passing over them. The hind limbs then begin to show, the front pair being hidden in the gill-chambers. The lungs, developed from the gullet, get to work at the same time as the hind legs, and the tadpole, about nine weeks old, rises to the surface to breathe air direct and feeds greedily on the water weeds. This is followed by a period when it seems to have no relish for its food, the tail shortens, the horny jaws are lost, the frills on the lips shrink, the mouth widens, the tongue grows larger, the eyes come through the skin, and the fore legs appear, one through the gill aperture, the other through a hole it pushes for itself in the right opercular fold. Meanwhile the tadpole has begun to feed again, but has changed its diet; from being mainly a vegetarian it has become exclusively a carnivore, eager, when opportunity serves, to feed on younger tadpoles. And as it feeds the intestines become more and more adapted for dealing with animal food, the abdomen shrinks, the tail shrinks, the legs lengthen, and as a frog it leaves the water for the land, to return to it only in the breeding season and in times of danger.

The Common Frog is about three inches in length. It is almost any shade of brown above, with blackish spots, the males being yellowish white below and the females orange, the males being further recognisable by the black swollen cushion on the inner side of the first finger. The vocal sacs are internal, and when in use bulge out the skin of the throat below the angle of the mouth. It ranges over the whole of Europe and right across Africa.

The Edible Frog is rather larger. It is greenish above, with a pale stripe down the middle of the back, the blackish markings being very distinct. The under parts are smooth, but on the upper parts are a few warts and glandular folds. The male is distinguishable by the grey pad on the inner side of the first finger, and by the external vocal sac behind the angle of the mouth, which is distended when used until it is almost as large as a cherry. It is more aquatic in its habits than the common species, and ranges further south and east, crossing the Mediterranean into Northern Africa, and appearing in Japan. In England it is confined to the eastern counties, while the common frog is found everywhere, even in Ireland. The common frog is the brown frog or grass-frog; the edible frog is the green frog or water-frog. Both feed on insects, worms, and snails, and other animals in a small way, not excepting younger frogs in all stages, these being flicked down the throat by the curious tongue, which is worked from the front of the mouth instead of from the back. The green frog has a much louder and more musical note than the brown frog, and his vocal efforts take the form of a regular series of solos and choruses.

Triton.   Plates xxxii. and xxxiii.   *CAUDATA.*

86.	*cristatus,*	CRESTED NEWT. Hind toes free; crest high and serrated, highest in middle; skin warty.
87.	*vulgaris,*	SMOOTH NEWT. Hind toes lobate or free; crest high and festooned, highest in front; skin smooth.
88.	*palmatus,*	WEBBED NEWT. Hind toes webbed; crest low and straight, highest behind; tail ending in a filament.

Newts have four fingers and five toes, and eyes with movable lids. They have teeth on the palate as well as in the jaws, the right and left series of palatal teeth meeting, or nearly meeting, at an angle, instead of being arranged in two sigmoid curves; and the tail is flat and not round, as in the salamanders to which they are closely allied.

The Crested Newt has a warty skin with pores on the head and along the sides. A fold of the skin passes under the throat like a collar. The tail is very flat, with sharp edges above and below. In the breeding season the male has a high, curved crest, with serrated edge along the back, and another along the top of the tail, the tail being edged with violet and streaked with silver. The upper parts are brown spotted with blackish, there being white spots on the sides; the colour of the under parts is deep yellow spotted with black. The male is between five and six inches in length; the female is rather larger, and has an orange stripe along the bottom of the tail. The iris is golden yellow, and the toes are yellow, with black rings. The eggs are laid in the water, chiefly in May and June, or slightly earlier or later; they are protected from injury by being placed singly in a sort of sheath formed by folding together the leaves of grasses and other plants, a favourite one being *Veronica anagallis*. In shape they are spherical, with a white yolk and a firm capsule covered with adhesive matter, by which they are fastened to the leaf. As they swell they open the fold which protects them; in about a fortnight they are fully exposed to the water, and in another week the black-striped, yellowish-green tadpole emerges. It has a white edge to its tail, and three pairs of external feathery gills, and on its upper jaw are a couple of pairs of adhesive protuberances, by which it clings for support until it becomes strong enough to trust entirely to its swimming powers. It feeds freely on anything small, and soon begins to develop, but, unlike the frogs and toads, it grows its fore legs first, and not until it is three months old do its hind legs appear. As soon as both pairs are in working order the gills begin to shrink, and when the gills are closed the young newt comes ashore, half a year or more after leaving the egg; but not until three years have passed is a return made to the water, where the male first assumes his nuptial adornments, the full stature being reached at the conclusion of the fourth year. The Crested Newt takes to the water annually for about three months, and when it returns to the land, after the careful bestowal of the eggs, the handsome crest of the male is diminished to its normal size, and is without the bright colouration.

Every year in September—so it is reported—the newts of the neighbourhood hold a farewell meeting before retiring for hibernation. They then disperse to winter quarters, generally in clay, the youngsters each to a separate hole, those over three years old forming parties of from eight to a dozen to sleep through the winter together rolled up in clumps as large as a cricket ball. The retirement would seem to be due to scarcity of food rather than lowness of temperature, for newts have been frozen, experimentally, in solid blocks of ice and thawed out as lively as ever. They live on insects, worms, tadpoles, and so on, and with a fine sporting instinct never touch their prey unless it is alive and on the move; unlike toads they do not attack worms in the middle, but seize them by the head and swallow them lengthways, so that the worm's own bristles help it down to die. The Crested Newt ranges from Scotland and southern Sweden into south-western Asia. In south-western Europe it is replaced by the Marbled Newt.

The Smooth Newt is the commonest of the family in these islands. Its skin is smooth, not warty, and there are two rows of pores on the top of the head, and a few in an indistinct row along the sides. The upper parts are brownish grey, spotted with black, the spots being in lines, those on the head numbering five, the spots extending on to the festooned crest. The under parts are yellow spotted with black, the female having fewer and fainter markings than the male. The lower edge of her tail is orange, that of her mate is red, and his tail has a blue stripe along the side. He is about three and a quarter inches long, she is rather larger, and his hind toes are lobate, that is, fringed with membrane. Unlike the Crested Newt, this species lays its eggs in strings of four or six at a time, and attaches them to the roots of the water-plants instead of their leaves, and, instead of having two black stripes on the back, the tadpoles are dotted with yellow. In development, habits, food, and distribution it resembles the Crested Newt, except that it ranges into Ireland, where, although quite harmless like the others, it is credited with all sorts of misdeeds and evil influences.

The Webbed Newt is olive brown above and yellow below, the head being streaked and the body dotted with dark brown. The tail is truncate, and ends in a filament, and its under surface is blue in the male and orange in the female. The toes of the male are webbed and blackish. The female rarely exceeds three inches in length, the male being smaller and darker in colour. Another distinctive feature of this species is the flattened back with the two raised lateral lines passing above the eyes and extending all along the body, and another is the low continuous crest which begins rather far back on the neck. Like all the newts it swims with its tail, not with its legs, which it keeps close to the sides, and it sheds its skin frequently, and becomes much duller in hue during its nine months on land. It is confined to Western Europe, and ranges into Scotland, and is the rarest of the three.

As before we must have a list of the more important of the alternative names arranged alphabetically under the respective genera.

Bufo alpinus, 84
Bufo calamita, 85
Bufo cinereus, 84
Bufo cruciatus, 85
Bufo fœtidissima. 85
Bufo palmarum, 84
Bufo rubeta, 85
Bufo terrestris, 84
Bufo vulgaris, 84

Lacerta aquatica, 86, 87
Lacerta lacustris, 86
Lacerta maculata, 87
Lacerta palustris, 86
Lacerta salamandra, 87
Lacerta triton, 87
Lacerta vulgaris, 87
Lissotriton palmatus, 87
Lissotriton palimpes, 88
Lissotriton punctatus, 87
Lophinus palmatus, 88
Lophinus punctatus, 87

Molge cinerea, 87
Molge cristata, 86
Molge palmata, 87
Molge palustris, 86
Molge punctata, 87
Molge vulgaris, 87

Rana alpina, 83
Rana aquatica, 82
Rana bufo, 84
Rana esculenta, 83
Rana hispanica, 83
Rana maritima, 83
Rana mephitica, 85

Rana muta, 82
Rana palimpes, 83
Rana portentosa, 85
Rana rubeta, 84
Rana scotica, 82
Rana temporaria, 82
Rana viridis, 83

Salamandra abdominalis, 88
Salamandra aquatica, 86
Salamandra cincta, 88
Salamandra cristata, 86
Salamandra elegans, 87
Salamandra exigua, 87
Salamandra laticauda, 86
Salamandra palmata, 17, 88
Salamandra palimpes, 87
Salamandra palustris, 86, 87
Salamandra punctata, 87
Salamandra platyura, 86
Salamandra tæniata, 87

Triton aquaticus, 87
Triton asper, 86
Triton bibroni, 86
Triton carnifex, 86
Triton cristatus, 86
Triton exiguus, 87
Triton lævis, 87
Triton lobatus, 87
Triton marmoratus, 86
Triton minor, 88
Triton palmatus, 88
Triton palustris, 86, 87
Triton parisinus, 87
Triton punctatus, 87
Triton vulgaris, 87

The British amphibians of the past are represented by about three dozen species, a number so small that considerable additions would seem to be inevitable. None at all have been found below the Carboniferous system, but that series of rocks has yielded twenty species, while the Permian has yielded two, the Trias seven, and the Rhætics one, *Metopias diagnosticus* from Aust Cliff, which is the last, as yet, of our extinct amphibians. The succeeding formations have yielded none until we get to the Forest Bed, where we meet with the Toad, the Crested Newt, the Edible Frog, and the Common Frog; but these are confined to this bed, and no amphibian has up to the present been found in deposits of more recent date, a state of affairs evidently due more to non-discovery than to peculiar distribution.

Herewith is a list of

BRITISH AMPHIBIANS PAST AND PRESENT.

ECAUDATA.

RANIDÆ.

82. Rana temporaria (Forest Bed and Existent), Common Frog.
83. Rana esculenta (Forest Bed and Existent), Edible Frog.

BUFONIDÆ.

84. Bufo vulgaris (Forest Bed and Existent), Common Toad.
85. Bufo calamita (Existent), Natterjack.

CAUDATA.

SALAMANDRIDÆ.

86. Triton cristatus (Forest Bed and Existent), Crested Newt.
87. Triton vulgaris (Existent), Smooth Newt.
88. Triton palmatus (Existent), Webbed Newt.

LABYRINTHODONTA.

MASTODONSAURIDÆ.

Mastodonsaurus giganteus (Keuper).
Mastodonsaurus pachygnathus (Keuper).
Labyrinthodon laniarius (Keuper).
Labyrinthodon lavisi (Keuper).
Labyrinthodon leptognathus (Keuper).
Labyrinthodon ventricosus (Trias).
Diadetognathus varvicensis (Keuper).
Metopias diagnosticus (Rhætic).

ANTHRACOSAURIDÆ.

Anthracosaurus edgei (Coal Measures).
Anthracosaurus russelli (Coal Measures).
Loxomma allmanni (Carboniferous).
Dasyceps bucklandi (Permian).
Megalerpeton plicidens (Coal Measures),
Megalerpeton simplex (Coal Measures).

K

NYRANIDÆ.

Erpetocephalus rugosus (Coal Measures).
Ichthyerpeton bradleyæ (Coal Measures).
Ichthyerpeton hibernicum (Coal Measures).

ARCHÆGOSAURIDÆ.

Pholidogaster pisciformis (Lower Carboniferous).
Pholiderpeton scutigerum (Coal Measures).

MICROSAURIA.

UROCORDYLIDÆ.

Urocordylus reticulatus (Coal Measures).
Urocordylus wandesfordi (Coal Measures).
Keraterpeton galvani (Coal Measures).
Lepterpeton dobbsi (Coal Measures).

DOLICHOSOMATIDÆ.

Dolichosoma emersoni (Coal Measures).
Ophiderpeton brownriggi (Coal Measures).

BRANCHIOSAURIA.

PROTRITONIDÆ.

Batrachiderpeton lineatum (Coal Measures).
Pteroplax brevicornis (Coal Measures).
Pteroplax cornuta (Coal Measures).
Anthrakerpeton crassosteum (Coal Measures).
Lepidotosaurus duffi (Magnesian Limestone).

CHAPTER IX.
GLOSSARY,

———◆———

ABDOMEN, the part of the body between the thorax and the extremity of the pelvis.

ACETABULUM, the socket of the hip-joint in vertebrates ; in invertebrates, a fleshy sucker on the arm of a cephalopod.

ACROMION, the curved, flattened process of the mesoscapula or spine of the shoulder-blade.

ALISPHENOID, one of the greater wings of the sphenoid bone of the skull.

ALVEOLUS, a socket, as of the teeth.

AMPHICŒLOUS, concave at both ends.

ANAPOPHYSIS, the lower and more slender backwardly projecting process of the neural arch.

ANCHYLOSIS, the same as ankylosis.

ANGULARE, the principal element of the lower jaw in the tailless amphibians.

ANGULO-SPLENIAL, the inner element of the lower jaw in the tailed amphibians.

ANKYLOSIS, the coalescence of two bones so that they become immovably united.

ANNULARIS, the third finger.

ANOUROUS, having no tail.

ANTERIOR, in the fore part.

ANTIBRACHIAL MEMBRANE, that part of a bat's wing which extends above the arm.

ANTIBRACHIUM, the fore arm consisting of two bones, the radius and the ulna.

ARTICULATED, jointed.

ASTRAGALUS, the ankle bone immediately below the tibia.

ATLAS, the first of the neck vertebræ, the one on which the head is carried.

AXIS, the second of the neck vertebræ, that on which the skull and atlas rotate.

BASI-DORSALIA, the vertebral elements forming the neural arch in reptiles.

BASIHYAL, the outermost of the bones of the tongue.

BASI-OCCIPITAL, the bone in the skull nearest to the axis of the vertebral column.

BASI-SPHENOID, the bone in the skull immediately in front of the basi-occipital.

BICUSPIDS, the premolar teeth.

BRACHIUM, the upper arm.

BRACHYODONT, having short crowns and long roots (applied to teeth).

BUCCAL, pertaining to the mouth cavity or to the cheeks.

BULLA, the dilated portion of the tympanic bone in which the ear-drum is stretched.

BUNODONT, having tuberculated crowns (applied to teeth).

BURR, the annular excrescence at the base of the antler.

CÆCUM, the blind intestine.

CALCANEUM, the heel bone.

CALCAR, a projecting spur, as that from the heel in the bats.

CANINE, the eye tooth, the conical tooth placed between the incisors and premolars.

CANNON BONES, the representatives of the metacarpals or meta-tarsals in the ungulates.

CAPITULUM, the inferior and anterior head of the rib by which the attachment is made with the body of the vertebra.

CARAPACE, the upper shell of a chelonian.

CARNASSIALS, the sectorials or flesh teeth.

CARPALIA, the second row of wrist bones, consisting of the trapezium, trapezoid, magnum, and unciform, the last of which represents the fourth and fifth carpalia.

CARPUS, the wrist, formed by a series of bones joining on to the radius and ulna.

CAUDAL, pertaining to the tail.

CENTRALE, the central of the second row of wrist bones: the navicular bone in the ankle.

CENTRUM, the body or central portion of a vertebra.

CEPHALIC, pertaining to the head.

CERATOHYALS, the two bones in the tongue connecting the basi-hyal with the epihyal.

CERVICALS, the vertebræ of the neck.

CHEVRON BONES, the bones placed opposite to the intervertebral spaces on the under surface of the caudal vertebræ.

CINGULUM, the rim surrounding the crown of the tooth.

CLAVICLE, the collar bone joining the shoulder bone to the breast bone, and lying in front of the coracoid.

COCCYX, the united vertebræ at the end of the backbone.

CONDYLE, a knob-like eminence bearing a flattened articular surface.

CORACOID, the bone in the shoulder girdle beneath the scapula, generally rudimentary in mammals, but well developed in birds and reptiles.

CORONOID, the curved process on the upper border of the lower jaw to which the temporal muscle is attached, also the raised ridge at the upper joint of the ulna.

COTYLOID, the fibro-cartilaginous ring round the margin of the acetabulum of the hip-joint.

CRANIUM, the bony case enclosing the brain formed by the union of several components.

CREPUSCULAR, pertaining to twilight.

CRIBRIFORM, with perforations like those of a sieve.

CRINIGEROUS, bearing hairs, hairy.

CUBOID, the outer of the four bones in the second row in the ankle.

CUNEIFORM, the wrist bone nearest to the ulna in a line with the fourth digit; the name given to three of the four bones in the second row of the ankle.

CUSPS, the prominences on the upper surface of a tooth.

DENTARY, the bone in the lower jaw which carries the teeth.

DENTINAL, pertaining to dentine.

DERMAL, pertaining to the skin.

DEXTRAL, from right to left.

DIAPHRAGM, the midriff, the muscular partition between the thorax and the abdomen.

DIAPOPHYSIS, the upper transverse process of a vertebra.

DIASTEMA, the interval between a series of teeth, as in the jaw of the cattle and deer.

DIGITIGRADE, walking on the tips of the toes.

DIGITS, the fingers or toes.

DIPHYODONT, having the permanent teeth preceded by a set of milk teeth.

DISTAL, furthest from the body.

DIURNAL, pertaining to daylight.

DORSAL, pertaining to the back.

DORSO-LUMBAR, pertaining to the back and loins taken together.

DUODENUM, the first portion of the small intestines.

EARLET, the tragus or subsidiary ear-conch, distinctive of some of the bats.

ENDOSTEAL, beginning within the substance of the cartilage.

ENSIFORM, shaped like a sword.

EPICORACOID, the inner prolongation of the coracoid.

EPIDERMAL, pertaining to the outer skin.

EPIGASTRIC, pertaining to the upper part of the abdomen.

EPIHYALS, the bones in the tongue and neck connecting the ceratohyals with the stylohyals.

EPIOTIC, the upper bone or cartilage encasing the organ of hearing.

EPIPHYSIS, a separate cartilaginous process eventually ossified into an adjoining expanse of bone.

EPISTERNUM, another name for the omosternum, the piece of cartilage at the inner end of the clavicle.

EPISTROPHEUS, another name for the axis, otherwise the second of the neck vertebræ.

ETHMO-TURBINAL, the front bone of the nasal cavity.

ETHMOID, the sieve-like bone at the root of the nose.

EXOCCIPITALS, the bones in the skull on each side of the basi-occipitals.

FABELLÆ, small bones lying behind the condyles of the femur.

FACET, a flat surface with a definite boundary.

FALCIFORM, the radial sesamoid bone of the wrist lying outside the line of the first digit.

FANGS, the poison teeth of the snakes.

FAUNA, the animals found within any particular district or area.

FIBULA, the smaller of the two bones in the leg below the knee, corresponding to the ulna in the arm.

FIBULARE, the calcaneum or heel-bone.

FLESH TEETH, the last upper premolar and the first lower molar, as modified for flesh-eating in the carnivores.

FLUKES, the two blades of the tail in cetaceans.

FONTANELLE, a gap or vacancy.

FOOT-PADS, the prominences on the tread of the foot which come in contact with the ground.

FORAMEN, a hole or perforation.

FOSSA, a pit or depression.

FRONTAL SINUS, the cavity in the fore part of the frontal bone in the skull.

FRONTALS, the bones above the orbito-sphenoids closing in the cerebral cavity in front and above.

FRUGIVOROUS, feeding on fruit.

FUSIFORM, spindle-shaped.

FURCATE, divided into two branches.

GLENOID FOSSA, the concave under surface of the squamosal in which the condyle of the lower jaw articulates; also the articular surface of the scapula.

GLOSSOHYAL, the median process of the basihyal.

HÆMAL, pertaining to the blood.

HABITAT, the natural place of permanent abode.

HALLUX, the great toe, the innermost of the five digits of the foot, corresponding to the pollex in the hand.

HETERODONT, having teeth of different characters.

HIP GIRDLE, the pelvic girdle formed of the two innominate bones, or their separate components, carrying the hind limbs.

HUMERUS, the bone of the upper arm.

HYOID, pertaining to the tongue and neck; the bone supporting the tongue.

HYOMANDIBULAR, the ossified upper portion of the hyoid bone in fishes.

HYPAPOPHYSIS, the central process projecting downwards from the ventral surface of the vertebra.

HYPOCONE, the fourth primary cusp of an upper tooth.

HYPOCONID, the fourth primary cusp of a lower tooth.

HYPSODONT, having the crown of the tooth long and the root short.

ILIUM, the haunch-bone, the bone in the hip girdle which corresponds to the scapula in the shoulder girdle.

IMBRICATED, overlapping.

INCISORS, the front teeth in the mammalian jaw.

INCUS, the middle bone of the ear:

INDEX, the first finger.

INGUINAL, pertaining to the groin.

INNOMINATE bones, the two halves of the hip girdle each consisting of the ilium, pubis, and ischium.

INTERCLAVICLE, the lower prolongation of the clavicle, as in the monotremes.

INTERMAXILLA, the same as the premaxilla.

INTERMEDIUM, the wrist bone in the angle between the radius and ulna; also one of the constituent bones of the astragalus.

INTERPARIETAL, the apparent anterior prolongation of the upper end of the supra-occipital.

INTERVENTRALIA, the vertebral elements forming the centrum in reptiles.

ISCHIUM, the bone in the hip girdle on which we sit. It corresponds to the coracoid in the shoulder girdle.

JUGAL, another name for the malar or cheek bone.

JUGULAR, pertaining to the neck or throat.

LABIAL SHIELDS, the plates around a snake's lips.

LACHRYMAL, the bone between the ascending process of the palatine, the maxilla, and the frontal.

LAMELLIFORM, shaped like a thin plate.

LAMINATED, made up of thin plates.

LAMINÆ, the upper portions of the sides of the neural arch.

LARYNX, the upper part of the windpipe, situated beneath the hyoid bone.

LIGULATE, strap-shaped.

LOINS, the space between the lowest of the false ribs and the ilium.

LOPHODONT, having the tooth traversed by ridges, generally across the width of the jaw.

LUMBAR, pertaining to the loins.

LUNAR, the crescentic wrist bone lying nearest to the radius in a line with the third digit.

MAGNUM, the wrist bone lying in front of the lunar and centrale.

MALAR, another name for the jugal, the bone articulating with the maxilla and the zygomatic process of the squamosal.

MALLEUS, the outermost of the bones of the ear.

MAMMÆ, the paps or breasts.

MANDIBLE, the principal bone of the lower jaw.

MANUBRIUM, the presternum.

MAXILLA, the principal bone of the upper jaw.

MAXILLO-TURBINAL, the smaller bone of the nasal cavity.

MEATUS, an opening or passage.

MEDIUS, the middle finger.

MESETHMOID, the ossified or cartilaginous segment in front of the pre-sphenoid.

MESOSCAPULA, the outwardly projecting plate of the scapula.

MESOSTERNUM, the body of the breastbone, having the pre-sternum at the fore end and the xiphisternum at the hinder end.

METACARPALS, the series of bones at the root of the hand between the carpals and the phalanges.

METACONE, the inner primary cusp of an upper tooth.

METACONID, the inner primary cusp of a lower tooth.

METACROMION, the hinder diverging process of the acromion.

METAPODIALS, the metacarpals and metatarsals.

METAPOPHYSIS, the mammillary process, the upper accessory process of the neural arch which projects forwards and outwards.

METAPTERYGOID, the separate ascending portion of the quadrate.

METATARSALS, the series of bones between the tarsals and the phalanges.

MINIMUS, the fourth, or little, finger.

MOLARS, the back teeth or grinders.

MONOCONODONT, having but one cusp to the tooth.

MONOPHYODONT, having no milk teeth, aad consequently having only one set instead of two.

MUZZLE, the mouth and adjacent parts.

NARIAL, pertaining to the nostrils.

NASAL, the bone whose hinder end rests upon the nasal process of the frontal.

NAVICULAR, the ankle bone lying between the astragalus, the cuboid, and the cuneiforms.

NECK OF A RIB, the portion of the rib between the capitulum and the tubercle.

NEURAL ARCH, the arch formed by the processes which rise on each side from the dorsal surface of the centrum of a vertebra.

NEURAL SPINE, the process that projects upwards from the crown of the neural arch.

OCCIPITAL, the bone at the lower and hinder part of the cranium.

OCCIPUT, the hinder portion of the head.

ODONTOID, the centrum of the atlas.

OLECRANON, the process at the the upper end of the ulna to which the extensor muscles of the fore arm are attached.

OMOSTERNUM, the cartilaginous body at the sternal end of the clavicle.

OPISTHOCŒLUS, concave behind and convex in front.

OPISTHOTIC, the lower bone or cartilage encasing the organ of hearing.

ORBITO-SPHENOID, one of the lesser wings of the sphenoid bone of the skull.

OSSICLES, small bones.

OVIPAROUS, bringing forth the young in the egg.

OVOVIVIPAROUS, retaining the eggs in the body until the young are hatched.

PALATAL, pertaining to the palate.

PALATINE, the bone attached to the fore part of the pterygoid and forming the outer wall of the nasal canal.

PALMATED, flattened out like the palm of the hand.

PAPILLA, a small, soft prominence generally adapted for delicate sensation.

PARACONE, the outer primary cusp of an upper tooth.

PARACONID, the outer primary cusp of a lower tooth.

PARAPOPHYSIS, the lower transverse process of a vertebra.

PARIETALS, the bones placed next above the alisphenoids.

PAROCCIPITAL, the prominent process for muscular attachment placed externally to the occipital condyle.

PATAGIUM, the wing membrane of the bats and flying squirrels.

PATELLA, the knee-cap.

PECTORAL GIRDLE, the shoulder girdle.

PEDICLES, the processes on the frontal bones from which the antlers are developed and shed; the lower portions of the sides of the neural arch.

PELVIC GIRDLE, the hip girdle, formed of the two innominate bones or their components.

PELVIS, the bony ring formed by the innominate bones or their components and the sacrum.

PERIOTIC, the bone in which is the internal ear.

PHALANGES, the bones of the digits either of the hand or foot.

PHARYNX, the commencement of the gullet.

PISIFORM, the outer bone of the wrist nearest to the ulna.

PLANTIGRADE, planting the whole sole of the foot on the ground.

PLASTRON, the lower part of the shell of a chelonian.

POLLEX, the thumb or first digit of the hand.

PORIFEROUS, bearing pores.

POST-FRONTAL, the separate hinder portion of the frontal.

POSTORBITAL, a process extending backwards from the frontal bone, marking the division between the orbit and the temporal fossa.

POSTSCAPULA, the backwardly projecting plate of the scapula.

PREFRONTAL, the separate fore portion of the frontal lying between the frontal and the lachrymal.

PREMOLARS, the teeth placed between the canine and the molars.

PRESCAPULA, the forwardly projecting plate of the scapula.

PREMAXILLA, the bone placed immediately in front of the maxilla.

PRENASAL, the bone at the outer end of the mesethmoid which strengthens the cartilaginous snout in the swine.

PRESPHENOID, the bone in the skull immediately in front of the basi-sphenoid.

PRESTERNUM, the fore part of the sternum to which the clavicle is attached.

PROCESS, a projection.

PROCŒLOUS, concave in front.

PRO-OSTEA, the two diverging horns of the presternum.

PRO-OTIC, the front bone or cartilage encasing the organ of hearing.

PROTOCONE, the central primary cusp of an upper tooth.

PROTOCONID, the central primary cusp of a lower tooth.

PROXIMAL, nearest to the body.

PTEROTIC, the bone or cartilage between the pro-otic and epiotic, being the lamelliform expansion of the upper edge of the periotic.

PTERYGOID, the bone attached to the lower surface of the basi-sphenoid and pre-sphenoid.

PUBIC, pertaining to the pubis.

PUBIS, the share-bone, the front bar of the lower component of the innominate bone in the pelvic arch.

QUADRATE, the squarish bone at the junction of the jaws in birds, reptiles and fishes.

QUADRATO-JUGAL, the bone formed by the union of the quadrate with the jugal.

RADIALE, the wrist bone joining on to the radius.

RADIUS, the long bone in the fore arm in line with the thumb.

RAMUS, a term for either right or left half of the lower jaw.

RECTUM, the last of the large intestines.

ROSTRAL, pertaining to the beak.

ROSTRUM, the beak formed in the cetaceans by the premaxillæ and maxillæ surrounding the vomer and mesethmoid cartilage.

SACRAL, pertaining to the sacrum.

SACRUM, the single bone formed by the ankylosis of the vertebræ between the lumbar and caudal regions of the backbone to which the haunch-bones are attached to form the pelvis.

SCAPHOID, the wrist bone nearest to the radius in a line with the second digit.

SCAPULA, the bone generally known as the shoulder blade or shoulder-bone.

SCUTE, a scale or shield such as those developed for protective purposes among reptiles.

SECTORIALS, the flesh teeth, more generally known as the carnassials.

SELENODONT, having the teeth with crescentic crowns.

SEMI-RETRACTILE, capable of being drawn back about half-way.

SEPTUM, a partition.

SERRATED, having notches on the edge, as the teeth on a saw.

SESAMOIDS, the small bones like seeds of grain in shape which are found in the hand and foot.

SHOULDER-GIRDLE, the bones consisting of the scapula, clavicle, etc., by which the arm is attached to the vertebral column.

SIGMOID, a curve in the shape of the letter S.

SINUS, a hollow space or dilation.

SINISTRAL, from left to right.

SPHENOID, the wedge-shaped bone across the base of the skull.

SPLENIAL, the inner bone of the mandible adjacent to the dentary.

SQUAMOSAL, the scale-like bone in contact with the basi-occipital, parietal and alisphenoid.

STAPES, the innermost of the three bones of the ear.

STYLIFORM, slender and pointed.

STYLOHYALS, the bones in the tongue connecting the epihyals with the cranium.

SUPERCILIARY, pertaining to the eyebrow, the upper bony arch of the orbit.

SUPRA-OCCIPITAL, the bone in the skull above the basi-occipital.

SUTURE, the line of junction of component bones or other adjacent surfaces.

SYMPHYSIS, the union of two bones in which there is little or no movement.

SYNOVIA, the lubricating fluid secreted by the synovial membrane lining the joints of the bones.

TALON, the heel of a tooth.

TARSALIA, the five bones in the second row of the ankle, known otherwise as the cuneiforms and cuboid.

TARSUS, the ankle, instep, and heel.

THORACIC, pertaining to the thorax.

THORAX, the chest, the part of the body between the neck and abdomen; the portion of the skeleton enclosing it.

THYROHYALS, the bones in the tongue connecting the basi-hyal with the thyroid cartilage of the larynx.

TIBIA, the larger of the two bones in the lower leg, otherwise known as the shin-bone.

TINE, the prong of an antler.

TRACHEA, the windpipe.

TRAGUS, the earlet or eminence in front of the opening of the ear in certain bats.

TRANSPALATINE, the outer wing of the palatine joining the maxilla to the pterygoid.

TRAPEZIUM, the outer wrist bone joining on to the scaphoid and trapezoid and supporting the thumb.

TRAPEZOID, the wrist bone joining on to the centrale, scaphoid and trapezium.

TRICONODONT, having three cusps as in the case of molar teeth.

TROCHANTERS, the tuberosities at the upper end of the femur.

TROCHLEA, the articular surface at the lower end of the humerus.

TRUNCATED, abruptly cut short.

TUBERCLE, the point by which the rib is attached to the transverse process of the vertebra.

TUBERCULATED, bearing tubercles or cusps as in the case of molar teeth.

TUBULIFEROUS, perforated with small tubes.

TURBINALS, the two bones in the nasal cavity.

TYMPANUM, the ear-drum.

TYMPANIC, the lower bone on the outer side of the periotic.

TYMPANOHYAL, the small bone lying in the passage between the tympanic and periotic.

ULNA, the bone in the fore arm in line with the little finger.

ULNARE, the wrist-bone joining on to the ulna.

UMBILICUS, the navel.

UNCIFORM, the wrist bone lying in front of the cuneiform.

UNGUICULATE, furnished with claws.

UROSTYLE, the coccyx in the form of the central bar of the pelvic bones in the amphibians.

VENTRAL, pertaining to the under surface as opposed to the dorsal or upper surface.

VERTEBRA, any one of the bony segments of which the backbone consists. VERTEBRÆ, two or more such segments.

VESTIGIAL, traceable in a rudimentary form.

VILLOSE, closely haired like the pile of velvet.

VISCERA, the internal organs.

VIVIPAROUS, bringing forth young free from the egg.

VOMER, the bone underlying the mesethmoid and the fore portion of the presphenoid.

WITHERS, the ridge between the root of the neck and the shoulder-bones.

XIPHISTERNUM, the ensiform process at the hinder end of the breastbone.

ZYGANTHRUM, the process on the back of a snake's vertebra which works on the zygosphene of the adjoining vertebra.

ZYGAPOPHYSES, the projecting smooth surfaces by which the vertebræ are joined to each other.

ZYGOMATIC PROCESS, the process projecting from the squamosal and joining on to the malar.

ZYGOSPHENE, the process on the front of a snake's vertebra which works on the zyganthrum of the adjoining vertebra.

CHAPTER X.

SPECIFIC NAMES.

———◆———

THESE names are those of living species only. The numbers refer to the Coloured Plates, in the list of which will be found the systematic and popular names adopted throughout this book.

Abdominalis, Salamandra, 87, 88
Abietum, Martes, 23
Acutus, Delphinus, 70
Acutus, Lagenorhynchus, 70
Ædura, Lacerta, 76
Africanus, Vespertilio, 14
Agilis, Lacerta, 76, 77
Agrestis, Arvicola, 43
Agrestis, Microtus, 43
Agrestis, Mus, 43
Albicans, Balæna, 64
Albicauda, Phoca, 32
Albirostris, Delphinus, 69
Albirostris, Lagenorhynchus, 69
Albus, Lepus, 47
Alexandrinus, Mus, 41
Alopex, Canis, 22
Alopex, Vulpes, 22
Alpina, Rana, 83
Alpinus, Bufo, 84
Altivolans, Vespertilio, 7
Amphibia, Arvicola, 44
Amphibius, Arvicola, 44
Amphibius, Microtus, 44
Amphibius, Mus, 44
Annulata, Phoca, 31
Antiquorum, Balæna, 56
Antiquorum, Physalus, 56
Aquatica, Arvicola, 44
Aquatica, Lacerta, 86, 87
Aquatica Rana, 82
Aquatica, Salamandra, 86
Aquaticus, Triton, 87
Araneus, Sorex, 18
Arcticus, Leucopleurus, 70

Arcticus, Lepus, 47
Arenicola, Lacerta, 77
Asper, Triton, 86
Ater, Arvicola, 44
Atlantica, Dermatochelys, 74
Auritus, Plecotus, 3
Auritus, Vespertilio, 3
Australis, Balæna, 53
Austriaca, Coronella, 80
Austriacus, Coluber, 80
Avellanarius, Mus, 36
Avellanarius, Muscardinus, 35
Avellanarius, Myoxus, 35

Barbarus, Cervus, 50
Barbastellus Synotus, 4
Barbastellus, Vespertilio, 4
Bechsteini, Myotis, 13
Bechsteini, Vespertilio, 13
Beluga, Delphinapterus, 64
Berus, Coluber, 81
Berus, Pelias, 81
Berus, Viperus, 81
Bibroni, Triton, 86
Bicolor, Anguis, 75
Bicolor, Sorex, 20
Bidens, Mesoplodon, 61
Bidens, Physeter, 61
Bidentatus, Delphinus, 60
Bilineata, Lacerta, 78
Biscayensis, Balæna, 53
Bistriata, Lacerta, 78
Blythii, Vespertilio, 14
Boops, Balæna, 54
Boops, Megaptera, 64

First published as *Our Country's Animals* by Simpkin, Marshall,
Hamilton, Kent & Co. Ltd.

This edition published 1988 by Omega Books Ltd,
14 Greville Street, Hatton Garden, London EC1.

All rights reserved. This publication may not be
reproduced, stored in a retrieval system,
or transmitted, in any form or by any means, electronic,
mechanical, photocopying, recording or otherwise,
without the prior permission of the publishers.

ISBN 1-85007-019-9

Printed and bound in Spain by Gráficas Estella, Navarra.